PE

SI

Richard Quick was b lives in London. *Ju* *Sixteen Satires of Juvenal*, has been presented at the Bush theatre. He has written verse and parody for BBC Radio 4's *Week Ending*, and his other radio and television credits include *The News Huddlines, The Larger Lunacy of Stephen Leacock* and *Now Something Else*. *Simon's Bug* is his first book.

SIMON'S BUG

RICHARD QUICK

PENGUIN BOOKS

To Janie

PENGUIN BOOKS

Published by the Penguin Group
27 Wrights Lane, London W8 5TZ, England
Viking Penguin Inc., 40 West 23rd Street, New York, New York 10010, USA
Penguin Books Australia Ltd, Ringwood, Victoria, Australia
Penguin Books Canada Ltd, 2801 John Street, Markham, Ontario, Canada L3R 1B4
Penguin Books (NZ) Ltd, 182–190 Wairau Road, Auckland 10, New Zealand

Penguin Books Ltd, Registered Offices: Harmondsworth, Middlesex, England

First published by Weidenfeld & Nicolson Ltd 1988
Published in Penguin Books 1989
1 3 5 7 9 10 8 6 4 2

Printed and bound in Great Britain by
Cox & Wyman Ltd, Reading

A TRANSCRIPTION OF ALL INCOMING/OUTGOING TELEPHONE CALLS ON (NUMBER WITHHELD)

6 MARCH–2 APRIL

SUBSCRIBER:

SIMON WEBB
24 Tufnell Park Terrace, London N7

TRANSCRIPTION BY:

RORY WEBB

THURSDAY 6 MARCH

CALL 1 – TIMED 20.18

SIMON WEBB:
(ANSWERING) Hello?
MICHAEL WEBB:
Simon? It's Michael.

SIMON . . . Yes.
MICHAEL . . . Had a result?
SIMON . . . Sorry?
MICHAEL Your obscene caller.
SIMON . . . Nothing. . . . Nothing yet.
MICHAEL . . . Any probs with the monitor?
SIMON No, that's fine. . . . Yes. Yes, Joanna's very well.
MICHAEL Ah! . . . Joanna's there?
SIMON Yes.
MICHAEL . . . Right.
SIMON . . . Yes.
MICHAEL . . . Mustn't worry Joanna.
SIMON Exactly.
MICHAEL . . . Let me know when you get something on the tape.
SIMON Will do.
MICHAEL . . . Bye, then.
SIMON . . . Bye.

FRIDAY 7 MARCH

CALL 2 – TIMED 11.49

SIMON WEBB'S RECORDED ANSWER:
Hello. I'm afraid there's no one here to answer your call at the moment, but if you'd like to leave a message for Simon Webb, or *ToyJoys, Ltd*, please wait for the signal, speak as clearly as possible and do remember to mention your number. Thank you.
BLEEP
BOB PRENTICE:
I'd . . . uh . . . uh . . . Oh, bog off!

CALL 3 – TIMED 13.27 – THE SAME DAY

JOANNA WEBB:
(ANSWERING) Hello . . .
PIPS
Simon?
KIT WEBB:
Mum? . . . It's me.

JOANNA Kit, dear. How was the interview?
KIT Poxy! The job was naff anyway.
JOANNA . . . But you said . . .
KIT Packing postcards? . . . Four of us turned up. There was me, a weirdo with a swastika

tattooed on his cheek . . . one really ancient guy . . . and a creepy kid with a big gut, who stank of curry.

JOANNA . . . What happened?

KIT The creepy kid with the big gut landed it. He had references.

JOANNA Oh! . . . Are you coming straight back?

KIT I thought I might case Wanda. Yeah. She's found a new squat.

JOANNA All right, Kit. Go carefully.

KIT . . . Bye, now.

JOANNA . . . Goodbye, dear.

CALL 4 – TIMED 14.31 – THE SAME DAY

JOANNA WEBB:
(ANSWERING) Hello . . .
PIPS
SIMON WEBB:
Joanna?

JOANNA . . . How are you?

SIMON . . . Cold.

JOANNA Yes?

SIMON I'm not staying over, but I might be late. Anyone called?

JOANNA No. Someone got the *Ansafast* . . . but they phoned off.

SIMON Damn! I hate it when they don't say anything.

JOANNA . . . Yes.

SIMON . . . It's cold.

JOANNA Yes.

SIMON How was Kit's interview?

JOANNA . . . He needed references.

SIMON To pack postcards? God! Did you remind him to smile more?

JOANNA . . . Yes.

SIMON . . . It's damned cold!

JOANNA . . . Simon, I've picked up your prescription.
SIMON . . . They won't help.
JOANNA If you can only get a good night's sleep . . .
SIMON I'm *fine*, Joanna, absolutely *fine*.
PAUSE IN CONVERSATION – 6 SEC.
What a week!
JOANNA . . . Yes.
SIMON What a winter!
PIPS
. . . Bye.
JOANNA . . . Goodbye, Simon.

CALL 5 – TIMED 14.48 – THE SAME DAY

JOANNA WEBB:
(ANSWERING) Hello, (NUMBER WITHHELD).
BOB PRENTICE:
Oh! . . . Uh . . . Webb there?
JOANNA He's in Norwich all day, I'm afraid. Can I take a message?
BOB . . . I got the machine earlier. I'm not 'appy with the machines.
JOANNA . . . No?
BOB . . . Not really.
JOANNA I'm sorry nobody was here. My morning at *Oxfam*, and the lady who comes in today couldn't.
BOB . . . It's Bob Prentice.
JOANNA . . . Yes, Mr Prentice?
BOB I wrote it down for the machine. . . . Tell 'im . . . uh . . . Bob Prentice called.
JOANNA . . . Yes?
BOB . . . Yes.
JOANNA . . . Well, I'll certainly . . .
BOB There's an 'ang-up with the *Toddling Tots*.
JOANNA . . . I see.
BOB It's the toddling, really. They don't.
JOANNA Ah!

BOB Two dozen replacement *Toddling Tots*. Monday latest.

JOANNA . . . Right.

BOB Monday, *latest*!

DEAD LINE

CALL 6 – TIMED 15.09 – THE SAME DAY

SWITCHBOARD GIRL AT *COMPUTRON*:

Hello, *Computron International*. Could you hold the line, please?

JOANNA WEBB:

(PHONING OUT) Of course.

PAUSE IN CONVERSATION – 1 MIN 47 SEC.

GIRL So sorry to keep you waiting.

JOANNA I'd like to speak to Michael Webb, please.

GIRL Who's calling?

JOANNA . . . Joanna Webb.

GIRL I'll try for you. . . . Hold the line, please.

PAUSE IN CONVERSATION – 56 SEC.

I'm sorry, Mrs Webb, your husband's on another line at present. Could I ask him to phone you back, or would you like to hold? Preference, please?

JOANNA I'll hold, thank you. Actually, he's my brother-in . . .

GIRL Holding!

RECORDING OF *RAVEL'S BOLERO* STARTS – 42 SEC.

I'm so sorry, Mr Webb's still engaged.

RECORDING OF *RAVEL'S BOLERO* CONTINUES – 1 MIN 33 SEC.

JOANNA God help us!

RECORDING OF *RAVEL'S BOLERO* CONTINUES – 2 MIN 19 SEC.

GIRL I can put you through now.

JOANNA . . . Thank you. . . . I suppose there's no

chance of your changing that background tape. You've been using it . . .

MICHAEL WEBB:

Sorry, Joanna?

JOANNA	Michael! . . . I was just asking about the background tape.
MICHAEL	Yes, it does help, doesn't it?
JOANNA	. . . Yes.
MICHAEL	How are you?
JOANNA	I'm fine, fine. Michael . . . ? . . . *Simon*.
MICHAEL	. . . Yes?
JOANNA	I wouldn't mention it, of course, but you've seen quite a lot of him lately . . .
MICHAEL	. . . I suppose I have.
JOANNA	. . . He seems worried.
MICHAEL	Oh, no. Definitely not. No. Bit of pressure at work maybe.
JOANNA	Michael! . . . I wouldn't mention it, obviously, but last night he said he wanted to have a think and went down to the basement. Michael, the basement! There's no heating. We never go down in the basement.
MICHAEL	. . . If he said he wanted to . . .
JOANNA	He was down there an hour and a half. I could hear him whining and jumping up and down.
MICHAEL	. . . Whining?
JOANNA	. . . Cramp.
MICHAEL	Ah!
JOANNA	I really wouldn't mention it, but . . .
MICHAEL	Joanna . . . I must get to a meeting. . . . Look, trust me, yes? Simon's fine. . . . It's nothing to worry about.
JOANNA	. . . *What*'s nothing to . . . ?
MICHAEL	Must rush.
JOANNA	. . . But if there's . . .
MICHAEL	Bye.
JOANNA	. . . Yes . . . . . . Goodbye, Michael.

CALL 7 – TIMED 15.27 – THE SAME DAY

JOANNA WEBB:
(ANSWERING) Hello?
DANNY (SURNAME UNKNOWN):
Mrs Webb?

JOANNA . . . Yes?
DANNY It's Danny here. *Kwality Jools*. Your cufflinks are ready.
JOANNA . . . Excellent.
DANNY The engraving's rather good. We're talking gift-wrapped, I suppose?
JOANNA . . . Lovely. . . . I'll call in this afternoon.
DANNY We'll be waiting.
JOANNA . . . Thank you, Danny.

CALL 8 – TIMED 19.23 – THE SAME DAY

WANDA POOL:
Hi.
KIT WEBB:
(PHONING OUT) Wanda? It's Kit.

WANDA . . . Hi, Kit.
KIT Dad's still repping and mum's got a yoga class. You want to come round?
WANDA It's Friday. I'm squat cook.
KIT Oh, right, right. . . . Curry?
WANDA Curry.
KIT Yeah. I dropped by, but you weren't there.
WANDA . . . We'd run out of curry.
KIT Right.
WANDA What's been happening?
KIT . . . I had an interview this morning. Blew it!
WANDA Yeah? How come?
KIT I got the addresses muddled. Went to next Tuesday's. By the time I got to the right place, the manager had gone to lunch and

some doddery guy told me they'd filled the job anyway.

WANDA . . . That's really hard luck, Kit.

KIT Yeah. It's just, like . . . getting the address right.

WANDA Sure it is.

KIT . . . I bumped into Swastika Joe and Big Gut. They said the new squat's okay.

WANDA It's great! The squat's great! Big Gut's taken all the doors off and Swastika's aerosoled 'Home Sweet Home' on the draining-board.

KIT . . . Sounds good.

WANDA . . . Listen, it's sweet you called, but . . .

KIT Hey, someone told dad's *Ansafast* to bog off.

WANDA . . . Well, they would. I mean, that message! It's like he wants you to take the oath before spilling.

KIT Right.

WANDA That guy's solid! Can't you get him to wind down some?

KIT You can't talk to him any more, Wanda. Monday, I said to him, 'Monday's the dirtiest word in my diary.'

WANDA . . . Yeah?

KIT He said he hadn't realized I kept a diary.

WANDA Solid! . . . Look, I'm still with the curry.

KIT . . . Right.

WANDA See you.

KIT . . . I'll come by.

WANDA Sure. And stick with it.

KIT Yeah.

WANDA . . . Do so.

KIT I'll do so.

WANDA . . . Right.

KIT . . . When then?

WANDA Well . . . just drop by.

KIT Will do.

WANDA Yeah, what's so bad with Monday, if you're not working?

KIT Everyone else is.

WANDA Right. That's right.

KIT . . . Yeah.
WANDA . . . Sure.
KIT . . . Bye, Wanda.
WANDA . . . Chaio, now.

CALL 9 – TIMED 19.54 – THE SAME DAY

FERN WEBB:
(ANSWERING) Hello?
TANYA GRISEWOOD:
Fern! Fern, did you see it?

FERN Tanya?
TANYA . . . The Miles Ton video! Wow! Did you see it?
FERN . . . Why weren't you in school?
TANYA I didn't feel like school. *Fern*! Did you see the Miles Ton video?
FERN Yeah.
TANYA Wow!
FERN . . . I missed you.
TANYA Yeah? You know when he leaps into the green light, rips his shirt open, gets right up close and yells, 'I'm the *now*!' . . . then he runs up the ramp and stands looking away at the smoke?
FERN . . . Yeah?
TANYA He gets dimples in his bum.
FERN . . . Yeah?
TANYA It's the best!
FERN . . . Yeah.
TANYA . . . They think I'm in bed. Bye, Fern.
DEAD LINE

CALL 10 – TIMED 20.22 – THE SAME DAY

FERN WEBB:
(ANSWERING) Hello?

KATE AGNEW:
Fern? . . . Would that be Fern?

FERN	. . . Hi, gran.
KATE	How are you, dear?
FERN	. . . It's okay. No one's here, except Kit. We're postering.
KATE	. . . I'm sorry?
FERN	Pinning a Miles Ton pull-out over the rack-stacked.
KATE	. . . Well . . . you would be, dear.
FERN	. . . You want Kit?
KATE	Please.

PAUSE IN CONVERSATION – 53 SEC.

KIT WEBB:
Hello?

KATE	Kit, dear, we're coming down on Sunday.
KIT	. . . Yeah, mum said.
KATE	No, no. She'd invited us, but I'm now confirming that we're coming.
KIT	. . . I'll let her know.
KATE	Splendid. . . . And how's the quest for occupation?
KIT	. . . I had an interview.
KATE	An interview? That's excellent! Yes, excellent, dear.
KIT	. . . Yeah.
KATE	What was it for?
KIT	. . . Uh . . . retail management.
KATE	Excellent. I'll tell Ronald. When will you hear something?
KIT	Well . . . retail management . . . they don't take too long to make their minds up.
KATE	Splendid.
KIT	. . . Shall I ask mum to call? She's usually back elevenish.
KATE	No, no. I'll be halfway up the wooden hill.
KIT	. . . I'm sorry?
KATE	To Bedfordshire.
KIT	. . . Well . . . you would be, Kate.
KATE	. . . Goodbye, dear.
KIT	. . . Bye.

KATE . . . And congratulations.
KIT . . . Yeah.

CALL 11 – TIMED 23.56 – THE SAME DAY

SALLY WIMBUSH:
. . . *urrsch* . . .
SIMON WEBB:
(PHONING OUT) Sally?
SALLY Uh huh?
SIMON . . . Sorry, love. . . . Is Michael there?
SALLY He's . . . *eeeesh* . . . very much here. . . . *Your brother.*
MICHAEL WEBB:
. . . *ooooch* . . . Simon? . . . What time . . . ?
SIMON I wouldn't have phoned, but . . .
SALLY:
. . . *mmmmph* . . .
SIMON I've only just got back.
MICHAEL . . . Sorry, darling.
SALLY:
Don't be. . . . *ahhhsh* . . .
MICHAEL . . . ooooch . . .
SIMON . . . Michael? . . . Michael?
PAUSE IN CONVERSATION – 8 SEC.
Michael?
MICHAEL . . . Yes?
SALLY:
Yes!
SIMON . . . I know it's late, Michael, but it's important.
MICHAEL . . . You've . . . *urrsch* . . . something on the tape?
SIMON . . . No. . . . Curtis Pine.
MICHAEL . . . *mmmmph* . . .
SIMON He's with *Computron* . . . drives a Porsche, takes yoga classes.
SALLY:
. . . *ooooch* . . .

MICHAEL . . . the one with the hair . . . ? *urrsch* . . . in marketing?

SIMON That's him. Does he wear cufflinks?

MICHAEL . . . *What?*

SIMON . . . Cufflinks.

SALLY:

Don't move! *Just* . . . don't move!

MICHAEL *Cufflinks?*

SIMON . . . It's important.

MICHAEL Simon, have you been celebrating anything?

SALLY:

Don't . . . don't move!

SIMON . . . Look, check on Monday, could you?

SALLY:

Now . . . *move!*

MICHAEL Sure, I will.

SALLY:

EEEESH . . .

SIMON . . . Thanks, Michael.

SATURDAY 8 MARCH

CALL 12 – TIMED 10.17

BOB PRENTICE:
'Ello, *Little Tinkers*.
SIMON WEBB:
(PHONING OUT) Hello, Bob? Simon Webb.

BOB Thank the Lord!
SIMON These *Toddling Tots* . . .
BOB Monday, yes?
SIMON . . . Wednesday.
BOB Bugger Wednesday! I've 'ad three kids sobbing their guts up, and some Lady Muck of a mother . . . What a cow! She tried to nab the one in the window.
SIMON Ah, good. That one's working.
BOB That one! Walked a bleeding Marathon! I'd've cleared the lot if the rest didn't fall flat on their asses.
SIMON . . . I can make Wednesday.
BOB Look, chummy, I'm not bleeding . . . *I'LL BE RIGHT THERE, MY LITTLE DARLING*! . . . I'm not bleeding 'ere to be screwed about by bleeding *ToyJoys*.
SIMON . . . Wednesday.
BOB That's not . . .
DEAD LINE

CALL 13 – TIMED 11.23 – THE SAME DAY

FERN WEBB:
(ANSWERING) Hello?
TANYA GRISEWOOD:
Fern! Fern! You've got to come round tomorrow. Dad's cancelled his golf and we're barbecuing. Yeah! Dad's got a new one with three spits and he's really keen on barbecuing three things at once, and mum says we'll all have to wrap up well and pray. It's the best! Can you come?

FERN . . . Tomorrow? . . . We've got the grans.
TANYA Yeah, but listen, dad says we can put the speakers on the patio, 'cause the next-doors didn't take any notice when he told them about hoovering their hatch-back before breakfast.
FERN . . . I can't, Tanya. Mum wants to make a big fuss, just because gran's here for Mother's Day.
TANYA Yeah, Mother's Day! Dad says that's why he's barbecuing. D'you have to be there?
FERN I'll say.
TANYA Well, look, I'll . . . uh . . . I dunno what.
FERN . . . I am sorry, Tanya.
TANYA Wow! D'you think Georgina could come?
FERN . . . Georgina?
TANYA Hey, her mother died, didn't she?
FERN . . . Yeah, Last term.
TANYA Great! I'll phone Georgina. . . . Bye, Fern.
PAUSE IN CONVERSATION – 4 SEC.
FERN Bye.

CALL 14 – TIMED 12.02 – THE SAME DAY

MANAGERESS (?) IN FLORISTS:
Harlequin Florists.

JOANNA WEBB:
(PHONING OUT) Good morning . . .

MANAGERESS Good afternoon.

JOANNA What? . . . Oh, yes, I suppose it is. I wonder if I could reserve a small spray . . .

MANAGERESS Goodness me, no.

JOANNA . . . No?

MANAGERESS There's nothing I'm afraid. You do realize tomorrow's Mothering Sunday?

JOANNA Yes, of course. That's why . . .

MANAGERESS I am sorry, but we do seem to have left it till the very last moment, don't we?

JOANNA . . . Yes?

MANAGERESS Good afternoon.

CALL 15 – TIMED 12.26 – THE SAME DAY

KIT WEBB:
(ANSWERING) The Webb residence.

MICHAEL WEBB:
Kit? Hello, it's Michael.

KIT Hi, Michael.

MICHAEL Would that brother of mine be around?

KIT Sure. It's house-beautiful time. . . . *DAD*! . . . The grans are descending tomorrow and staying in Rory's room. Dad's trying to make it look habitable. He may be some while. . . . *DAD, IT'S MICHAEL*!

MICHAEL . . . How's life?

KIT . . . Yeah . . . life.

MICHAEL . . . Work?

KIT Not yet. Two *O Levels* make a pretty deadly CV.

MICHAEL Mmmm.

KIT Most of the jobs I go for, I'm over-qualified. . . . Here's dad.

SIMON WEBB:
Michael?

MICHAEL I'm not sure I cracked the code.
SIMON . . . Code?
MICHAEL *Cufflinks.*
SIMON Oh! . . . Sorry about phoning so late.
MICHAEL Phoning late was nothing. We were working on *cufflinks* till dawn.
SIMON Ah!
MICHAEL Around four-thirty Sally decided it was an anagram of *fun flicks.* Are we getting warm?
SIMON No, no. I mean . . . *Fern, go and help your mother with the Dettol.* . . . Yes . . . does Curtis Pine wear cufflinks?
MICHAEL Mmmm.
SIMON I just thought you'd be seeing him in the office and you could check.
MICHAEL What is this, Simon? You think Curtis makes obscene phone calls?
SIMON Not in so . . .
MICHAEL You think that workaholic finds time to phone you up and pant? Listen, Curtis may take facials, but frustrated he's not.
SIMON . . . He's not?
MICHAEL No. Randy little brat!
SIMON . . . Yes?
MICHAEL Yes.
SIMON Michael . . . just check.
MICHAEL . . . You've nothing on the tape yet?
SIMON . . . No.
MICHAEL . . . You're sure you're not letting all this get to you, Simon?
SIMON *Get* to me? Why *shouldn't* I let it *get* to me?
MICHAEL . . . Okay. . . . I'll check out Curtis, but . . .
SIMON Thanks, Michael.
MICHAEL . . . Bye, then.
SIMON . . . Bye.

CALL 16 – TIMED 12.49 – THE SAME DAY

FERN WEBB:
(PHONING OUT) . . . *think of anything else to do.*
HITLINE:
. . . so congratulations all round and never mind, Sharon. I'm sure you did your best. Coming up now for all concerned, it's Paul McIvory with *Flights of Fancy*. Hit the *Hitline*, Paul.
INSTRUMENTAL – 18 SEC.
PAUL McIVORY:

'Flights of fancy –
Flights of fancy –
Flights of fancy –
Flights of swans look rather lovely –
Flights of nuclear-warheads don't –
Flights of swans make life worth living –
Flights of nuclear-warheads won't.
Good is good and bad is awful –
Badness gets me so depressed –
Goodness makes you so much nicer –
Bad is bad and good is best.
Flights of fancy –
Flights of fancy
Always fill your head,
But those flights of fancy
Kill your cares,
Or kill you dead.

INSTRUMENTAL – 14 SEC

When you have that flight of fancy,
Only kill those little cares –
Dream a dream and not a nightmare,
When you climb that flight of stairs.
Good is good and bad is awful –
Badness gets me . . .'

DEAD LINE

CALL 17 – TIMED 13.11 – THE SAME DAY

KATE AGNEW:
Hello? Ludlow (NUMBER WITHHELD).
JOANNA WEBB:
(PHONING OUT) Mother, it's . . . *FERN, YOU'RE NOT TO GO INTO RORY'S* . . . . . . *THEN COME DOWN*! . . . Sorry, mother. Kit said you'd phoned.

KATE Yes, dear.
JOANNA . . . We're all thrilled you're coming.
KATE Yes, dear. What can we bring?
JOANNA . . . Don't go to any . . .
KATE We're frightfully well off in the garden department. Ronald's past coping with it and I simply won't. Never felt the need, dear. I thought some plants, maybe.
JOANNA . . . Mother, I really wouldn't . . .
KATE We might just pop something into the shooting-brake. . . . Joanna, Ronald was asking . . .
JOANNA *Not in the living-room, Fern!*
KATE Joanna?
JOANNA *We've only just* . . .
KATE Hello?
JOANNA . . . *How can she have all the luck if her mother's dead?*
KATE . . . Hello?
JOANNA . . . Sorry, mother.
KATE Yes. . . . Ronald wants to know if . . . uh . . . Simon's brother . . .
JOANNA . . . Michael?
KATE Yes, is he the same Michael Webb who's brought Satanism to Hereford? Ronald cut it out of the paper.
JOANNA . . . Of course he's not.
KATE Ronald's been showing the cutting to everyone and muttering about devil-worshippers infiltrating the family. And those poor girls!

JOANNA . . . Webb's a very common name, mother.

KATE . . . I'm well aware of that.

JOANNA . . . Michael wouldn't have any energy left for Satanism. He's devoted to computers.

KATE It does amount to virtually the same thing. We'll see you at one.

JOANNA . . . Lovely, mother.

KATE . . . Goodbye.

JOANNA . . . Have a good journey. . . . *FERN*!

CALL 18 – TIMED 14.36 – THE SAME DAY

ASSISTANT (?) IN FLORISTS:
. . . to write your own card. Yes, just along the little dots. . . . Hello, *Blooming Boo-K's.*

JOANNA WEBB:
(PHONING OUT) Good afternoon. I was wondering if there was any chance of some flowers. A small spray perhaps?

ASSISTANT *. . . if you'd like to try mine, I think it's . . .*
. . . they do . . . . . . ruins your bag if you're not . . . . . . leaked all over the lining . . . . . . four telly-licence stamps and a lipstick ruined . . .
. . . Blooming Boo-K's.

JOANNA Yes . . . A small spray.

ASSISTANT *. . . find a bin just there . . . of course, take another card . . . . . .* Hello?

JOANNA Hello. I was hoping I might be able to order a small spray. If you did have anything . . . roses, maybe? . . . I'd be so grateful.

ASSISTANT *. . . the thought after all, isn't it? . . . lovely . . .*
. . . sure she will . . . . . . Blooming Boo-K's.

JOANNA Would it be possible to order . . . ?

ASSISTANT No more phone orders, I'm afraid. . . . *really nice . . . . . . if you could let me have my . . .*
DEAD LINE

CALL 19 – TIMED 15.44 – THE SAME DAY

SAM WARMSLEY:
Hello, *Warmsley Floral Tributes*.
JOANNA WEBB:
(PHONING OUT) Mr Warmsley? . . . Sam? . . . It's Joanna Webb. You may remember me from a wedding bouquet you were kind enough to provide . . . uh . . . some while back.

SAM . . . Sorry, lady? Who d'you say?

JOANNA It's Joanna. Sam, you were the first person to come to mind. Would a small spray of flowers . . . ?

SAM *Flowers?* . . . What, *today?*

JOANNA . . . I'd be so grateful . . . Sam.

PAUSE IN CONVERSATION – 6 SEC.

SAM Okay, lady. We'll put something together.

JOANNA I suppose roses . . . ?

SAM It'll be our . . . uh . . . spring selection. If someone could drop in before five.

JOANNA Yes, yes. Hold on. . . . ***SIMON! SIMON, DON'T GO YET! . . . FORGET THE GATEAU! SAM WARMSLEY'S! . . . OF COURSE, YOU DO. THE SHOP IN CROYDON!***

SIMON WEBB:
CROYDON?

PAUSE IN CONVERSATION – 11 SEC.

JOANNA That'll be fine.

SAM . . . They'll be ready.

JOANNA . . . Thank you, Mr Warmsley.

CALL 20 – TIMED 17.19 – THE SAME DAY

WANDA POOL:
Hi.
KIT WEBB:
(PHONING OUT) Wanda? It's Kit?

WANDA . . . Hi, Kit.
KIT . . . I thought I might drop by.
WANDA Yeah? I'm just about to crash.
KIT Oh?
WANDA Big Gut and Swastika would love to see you. Jason came round this morning and started this really heavy session. He's analysing Gurdjieff.
KIT Yeah?
WANDA Yeah. . . . He's still talking.
KIT . . . I didn't know you were into Gurdjieff.
WANDA I'd never heard of Gurdjieff.
KIT Well, yeah . . . better crash then, Wanda.
WANDA Will do.
KIT . . . Maybe I'll drop by tomorrow.
WANDA Sure.
KIT . . . Bye, then.
WANDA . . . Chaio, now.

CALL 21 – TIMED 19.09 – THE SAME DAY

GEORGE MEADOWS:
Redhill (NUMBER WITHHELD).
SIMON WEBB:
(PHONING OUT) George?

GEORGE . . . Si? . . . Whahay! . . . Nice one.
SIMON How are you?
GEORGE You wanna know about *fit*? I'll tell you about *fit*.
SIMON . . . Fancy a jar?
GEORGE Tonight? Country and Western gig. No can do.
SIMON Ah!
GEORGE . . . Crying shame, Si.
SIMON . . . George . . . this might sound odd, but . . .
GEORGE . . . Shoot!
SIMON . . . If you think I'm being too personal . . .

GEORGE Shoot the personal!

PAUSE IN CONVERSATION – 4 SEC.

SIMON Gloria.

GEORGE *Gloria*? Bitch of the first water. You wanna know about *bitch*? I'll tell you about *bitch*. . . . You've seen her?

SIMON No, no. I was wondering . . . George, what made you first suspect? . . . You must have noticed . . . . . . little things.

GEORGE What little things?

SIMON . . . Something that made you realize she was . . .

GEORGE . . . Screwing around?

SIMON . . . Yes.

GEORGE Right. I found them on the carpet.

SIMON . . . Ah!

GEORGE Bollock naked.

SIMON . . . Yes, but before that . . . You must have noticed some small . . .

GEORGE Nope. I was still in love, dammit! I'd just bought her a pair of Rhinestone Cubans.

SIMON . . . I see.

GEORGE You wanna know about *love*? I'll tell you . . .

SIMON How about tomorrow night?

GEORGE Spot on!

SIMON . . . I'll be there.

GEORGE Whahay!

SIMON . . . Cheers, George.

GEORGE . . . Bye, Si.

SUNDAY 9 MARCH

CALL 22 – TIMED 08.33

SIMON WEBB'S RECORDED ANSWER:
Hi. Simon Webb here on (NUMBER WITHHELD). Want to leave a message for the Webb family, or *ToyJoys*? We'll be . . . uh . . . itching to hear it. Just lay it down after the bleep. Chaio, now.

BLEEP

KATE AGNEW:
Whatever . . . ? Uh . . . Joanna, dear? . . . I'm not sure I under . . . Joanna? . . . We're leaving now. It's about half past eight and we're leaving now. Ronald thought it wise to make an early start, so we should be there . . . well, twelve. . . . Not *one*, twelve. We'll be early, dear. . . . Was I all right?

CALL 23 – TIMED 11.14 – THE SAME DAY

SIMON WEBB:
(ANSWERING) Hello, Simon Webb.

SPANISH OPERATOR:
Are you (NUMBER WITHHELD)?

SIMON Yes. Could you hold on? . . . *FERN, TELL YOUR MOTHER I CAN'T CHECK THE ROAST, STOP*

THE ROOF LEAKING, FIND THE SINK-PLUNGER AND ANSWER THE PHONE AT THE SAME TIME. . . . Yes?

OPERATOR I have a transfer charge call from Barcelona. Will you accept the charges?

SIMON Oh, no! Not *now!* . . . No! . . . Are you Spanish?

OPERATOR . . . Yes, I am.

SIMON Your English is damned good.

OPERATOR . . . That's most kind. I take it you won't accept the charges?

SIMON Of course I'll accept the charges.

OPERATOR . . . The language, I understand. The people? *Ni hablar*. . . . Putting you through.

PAUSE IN CONVERSATION – 6 SEC.

RORY WEBB:

Hello?

SIMON Rory?

RORY Hi, dad. How are you?

SIMON Hard to say. Your grandmother's coming down for Mother's Day and your mother's going mad.

RORY Mother's Day! Ouch! I'd forgotten it existed.

SIMON No hope here. Kate phoned to tell us we'd be late. Listen, when are you getting back?

RORY . . . Dad . . . don't worry mum about this, but I've been done over.

SIMON . . . What?

RORY . . . Mugged.

SIMON *What*? . . . Are you all right?

RORY Not too bad. They didn't hurt me . . . much.

SIMON Thank God!

RORY They found my money-belt.

SIMON . . . What d'you lose?

RORY Pretty well everything I'd earnt. Dad, I wouldn't ask, but it's not going to be easy.

SIMON . . . How much?

RORY . . . Three hundred?

SIMON *Three hundred*? What? *Pounds*?

RORY . . . It's not that easy.

SIMON . . . When are you getting back?

RORY I'm thinking about it. . . . At the moment I can't afford a square meal, let alone travel.

SIMON Okay, I'll see what I can do. . . . Hold on. Your mother's here.

JOANNA WEBB:
Rory?

RORY Happy Mother's Day.

JOANNA Darling, it's so sweet of you to remember.

RORY . . . No problem.

JOANNA How are you? It was lovely to get the letter and the photographs. Who's Isabel? . . . *I know, Fern, but you're only making it worse. . . . In a moment. . . . JUST STOP SAYING THAT, SIMON!* . . . Rory?

RORY Uh huh?

JOANNA . . . She looked rather . . . Spanish.

RORY . . . She is Spanish.

JOANNA . . . Lovely.

RORY . . . Yes.

JOANNA When are you going to . . . ? *WHAT*?
Pause in conversation – 5 sec.
I CAN SEE IT'S COMING DOWN HARDER. . . .
Hello?

RORY . . . Hello.

JOANNA Rory, when are you . . . ? *THEY'RE UNDER THE . . . . . . I'M COMING!* . . . Oh, Kit wants a word.

RORY Fine.

JOANNA Lovely to speak to you, dear.

RORY . . . Sure.

KIT WEBB:
Hi, Rory.

RORY Kit! Great to hear you. Jeez! . . . Sounds like a good day not to be there.

KIT . . . Yeah.

RORY How are you making out?

KIT . . . Pass.

RORY You're still seeing Wanda?

KIT Sure.

RORY . . : Got there yet?

KIT . . . More or less.

RORY LAUGHS – 6 SEC.
KIT . . . Rory?
RORY . . . What's more or less?
KIT Wanda's a pretty sensitive girl.
RORY I never noticed. . . . Kit, you need to get away.
KIT I need a job, Rory. When are you . . . ? *Fern! We're not* . . . When are you getting back?
RORY . . . Things are good here, Kit.
KIT . . . Yeah?
RORY . . . Really good.
KIT . . . *AHHGH!* . . . *FERN!* . . . Rory? We'll see you, yeah?
RORY . . . Drop us a line.

FERN WEBB:
Rory? Rory, how are you? We got the *Polaroids*. You look really terrific, Rory. I showed them to Tanya and Tanya said you looked like a star, like you could be a real sound-engineer or something. Yeah! Tanya was going to have a barbecue, but it'll be rained off.It's the best! . . . When are you getting back?

RORY . . . Mmmm.

SIMON WEBB:
No! . . . *Yes, but I'm paying*! . . . Rory?

RORY . . . Hello.
SIMON Listen, I'll . . . . . . *THEN FIND ANOTHER BUCKET!* . . . Rory? I'll try and get some cash there, but come back. Yes? Repeat, come back! . . . *JOANNA, ANYONE CAN HAVE A LEAK!* . . . We'll see you soon, Rory.
RORY . . . Sure.
SIMON Bye, then.
RORY . . . *Adios*.

CALL 24 – TIMED 11.51 – THE SAME DAY

SIMON WEBB:
(ANSWERING) Hello, Simon . . .
PIPS
DEAD LINE
SIMON Damn! . . . *No, someone's trying to . . .*

CALL 25 – TIMED 11.54 – THE SAME DAY

SIMON WEBB:
(ANSWERING) Hello?
PIPS
SIMON *Joanna, it must be your . . .*
DEAD LINE
. . . If she's not here . . .

CALL 26 – TIMED 12.07 – THE SAME DAY

JOANNA WEBB:
(ANSWERING) Mother?
PIPS
KATE AGNEW:
Joanna?
JOANNA . . . Mother, where are you?
KATE . . . The shooting-brake's just not behaving, dear.
JOANNA . . . Oh?
KATE It's all these hills. Hills, everywhere, Joanna. We decided to come the pretty way.
JOANNA And *where* are you?
KATE I've no idea. We can't see a thing through the rain. . . . Do hold on a moment.

PAUSE IN CONVERSATION – 19 SEC.
Yes. Ronald thinks we've passed through Evesham.

JOANNA *Evesham*? . . . How is the car?

KATE Ronald's giving it a little rest, dear. We rather think it's an omen.

JOANNA Omen? . . . Mother, if the engine's . . .

KATE You never notice these signs, Joanna. Surely you remember the wedding?

JOANNA . . . What wedding, mother?

KATE *Your* wedding. The vicar had just reached that bit about 'to have and to hold', and your bouquet fell to pieces. . . . That's what I mean by an omen.

PIPS

JOANNA When might you arrive?

KATE . . . Joanna? I'm standing in a puddle!

JOANNA Just give me your *number*.

KATE Oh, I've no more . . . . . . Have you asked Simon whether his brother's still worshipping . . . ?

DEAD LINE

JOANNA . . . *Evesham . . . they think.*

CALL 27 – 13.43 – THE SAME DAY

TANYA GRISEWOOD:
Yeah?

FERN WEBB:
(PHONING OUT) Hi, Tanya.

TANYA Fern?

FERN It must be awful, Tanya. I mean, it must be awful with the storm and you wanting to have a barbecue.

TANYA . . . Yeah.

FERN I am sorry, Tanya. Did Georgina come?

TANYA No. . . . Her father was giving her a day

out. She said it was to take her mind off her mother being dead.

FERN Yeah? Wow! It must be awful with the barbecue being washed out, and Georgina not being there.

TANYA . . . Yeah.

FERN And no speakers on the patio! . . . Gran's broken down, so dad got us some great take-aways and mum says it won't be long before she has to chuck the roast out and let them go hungry. It's the best! Yeah, and the roof's leaking all over everything and Rory phoned up from Spain. He says he's even better looking now than he was in the *Polaroids* I showed you and I love him.

TANYA . . . That's nice, Fern.

FERN It's the best!

TANYA . . . Fern?

FERN Yeah?

TANYA . . . Nothing. . . . Bye.

FERN . . . Bye, Tanya.

CALL 28 – TIMED 16.24 – THE SAME DAY

SIMON WEBB:

(ANSWERING) Hello, Simon Webb.

PIPS

KATE AGNEW:

Hello?

SIMON . . . *Where* are you?

KATE Simon? You've no conception of travelling these days.

SIMON . . . Kate, you're *talking* to a . . . !

KATE We've found a garage.

SIMON . . . *Where* . . . ?

KATE You didn't wait lunch for us, did you?

PAUSE IN CONVERSATION – 3 SEC.

SIMON Where are you?

KATE Right outside the garage, dear. I'm not entirely sure you should have invited us. . . . One moment, Ronald's . . . . . . *YES, DEAR, PLAIN IF THEY HAVE IT, AND BARLEY-SUGARS, SOME MINTS* . . . . . . He's getting deafer than ever, Simon. I'll have to write it down. . . . *DO THEY STILL DO THE LOOSE EXTRA-STRONG ONES? JUST A QUARTER, IF* . . .

SIMON . . . God!

PAUSE IN CONVERSATION – 16 SEC.

PIPS

. . . Kate! . . . *Kate!*

DEAD LINE

CALL 28 – TIMED 18.52 – THE SAME DAY

GEORGE MEADOWS:
Redhill (NUMBER WITHHELD).
SIMON WEBB:
(PHONING OUT) George?

GEORGE Si, old son!

SIMON Sorry, George. Tonight's a no-go.

GEORGE . . . Crying shame.

SIMON Joanna's mother. ETA twelve noon and still not arrived.

GEORGE . . . Sucker!

SIMON . . . Tomorrow night?

GEORGE Spot on. . . . Si? . . . Somehow got the impression when you belled, you'd hit shite.

SIMON . . . I might have.

GEORGE You wanna know about *shite*, Si? I'll tell you about . . .

SIMON *JOANNA? . . . THEY'RE HERE! . . . FERN!*

GEORGE You've hit shite, Si?

SIMON . . . I've hit shite, George. . . . See you tomorrow.

GEORGE Whahay!

SIMON *KIT? GO AND WAKE YOUR MOTHER!*

GEORGE Attaboy!
SIMON FERN?

CALL 29 – TIMED 19.17 – THE SAME DAY

FRANCESCA(SURNAME UNKNOWN):
Pizza Eats. My name's Francesca. How can I help you?
SIMON WEBB:
(PHONING OUT) Can you deliver some grub?
FRANCESCA It's *Pizza Eats'* pleasure. What . . . uh . . . grub had you in mind?
SIMON . . . We were thinking of pizzas.
FRANCESCA *Pizzas*? . . . Really?
SIMON . . . What's going?
FRANCESCA Deep-pan, shallow-pan, Mozzarella, Napoletana, Margherita, Vesuvio, Fiorentina, Capricciosa, Garfaguana, Marinara, Primavera, or *Pan-of-the-Week*, Americana, small, medium, or large.
SIMON . . . They're pizzas?
FRANCESCA . . . Pizzas.
SIMON . . . Hold on.
PAUSE IN CONVERSATION – 23 SEC.
KIT WEBB:
Francesca? It's Kit Webb.
FRANCESCA Hi, Kit. Who's the moron?
KIT . . . Someone who just dropped by. Six assorted medium, yes?
FRANCESCA 24, Tufnell Park Terrace?
KIT Right.
FRANCESCA Stand by for *Pizza Eats*.
KIT . . . Cheers.

CALL 31 – TIMED 20.36 – THE SAME DAY

WANDA POOL:
Hi.
KIT WEBB:
(PHONING OUT) Wanda?

WANDA Hi, Kit. . . . Yeah. . . . I'm just cooking.

KIT . . . You cooked Friday.

WANDA Right. . . . Sunday should be Swastika Joe, but he hasn't got up yet. He says it was all the Gurdjieff.

KIT Yeah? Mum's keeping pizzas warm. The grans arrived seven hours late with an old estate-car full of garden. Ronald's still unloading shrubbery. . . . Their crock's a goner! I dunno . . . they're supposed to be here a few days. It may be forever.

WANDA . . . Hold on, Kit. I'll check the curry.
PAUSE IN CONVERSATION – 1 MIN 22 SEC.
Kit?

KIT Hi.

WANDA Big Gut says Jason's doing a talk-in tonight on the *I Ching*. It's at the *Three Flags*, if you want to go.

KIT . . . Are you going?

WANDA . . . None of us are going.

KIT Right. I really can't, Wanda. Things are pretty jittery here. Dad drove like hell to Croydon yesterday, just to pick up a bunch of poxy flowers for Kate. Kate walked in, said mother ought to change the flowers more often and put them straight down the waste-disposal.

WANDA . . . I've always wanted a waste-disposal.

KIT . . . Dad's sulking in the basement.

WANDA . . . Yeah?

KIT He's calling it his *Think Tank*. You know, he's put a lock on it, Wanda? Says he needs somewhere to call his own. I ask you, who'd want to visit him in the basement?

WANDA . . . I wouldn't know, Kit.

KIT . . . The grans brought him down a goose.

WANDA . . . Like . . . a goose?

KIT A life-size plaster goose. Ronald makes them for a garden-centre. He says they look really realistic if you stand them by a pond. Pond! . . . We haven't even had a garden since dad built the garage.

WANDA . . . Right.

KIT Ronald keeps going on about how deprived we must feel without a proper garden.

WANDA Yeah, I mean, space . . . Everyone needs space, Kit.

KIT Right.

WANDA . . . Yeah.

KIT Space. . . . There's not even much space indoors now with the plants everywhere.

WANDA . . . Yeah?

KIT Hey, dad's changed the message on his *Ansafast*.

WANDA . . . You talked him into it?

KIT I never mentioned it. He's flipping, Wanda. He said he wanted a more relaxed image. . . . I told him it sounded crap.

WANDA Yeah?

KIT He started to twitch.

WANDA Solid.

KIT . . . Wanda . . . I thought if I dropped around later tonight . . .

WANDA I don't think so, Kit.

KIT . . . No?

WANDA . . . I'm not sure I'm into more . . . talking.

KIT . . . No.

WANDA . . . Chaio, now.

KIT . . . Yeah.

CALL 32 – TIMED 21.59 – THE SAME DAY

***RUNAROUND MINIS'* CONTROLLER:**
. . . never do it in their own car, would they? . . . Runaround Minis.

SIMON WEBB:
(PHONING OUT) Could I book a car for tomorrow morning, please?

CONTROLLER . . . Address?

SIMON 24, Tufnell Park Terrace.

CONTROLLER *. . . consideration? If my kids did that . . .* . . . What time?

SIMON . . . Six-thirty.

CONTROLLER . . . Where's it for?

SIMON . . . Paddington.

CONTROLLER *. . . cleaning costs, off the road for two hours . . .* . . . Paddington.

SIMON Make sure the damned thing's on time, would you? It's an elderly couple. They started worrying about missing the train some time ago, so just get here, right?

CONTROLLER *. . . should have seen it!* . . . Thank you.

MONDAY 10 MARCH

CALL 33 – TIMED 6.38 – THE SAME DAY

SIMON WEBB:
(ANSWERING) Whah . . . ? . . . Whah . . . ?
***RUNAROUND MINIS'* CONTROLLER:**
Yes. . . . *Runaround Minis*. . . . Your car's outside. Driver's nearly knocked the door down.

SIMON . . . Whassat . . . ?
CONTROLLER . . . Get it together!
SIMON . . . Whah . . . ?
CONTROLLER Ah! . . . You're the elderly couple?
SIMON . . . Whassat . . . ?
CONTROLLER . . . Take your time, dearie. We'll see you right. . . . Just try and make it to the front-door . . .
DEAD LINE

CALL 34 – TIMED 8.28 – THE SAME DAY

JOANNA WEBB:
(ANSWERING) Hello, (NUMBER WITHHELD).
ALAN O'CONNELL:
. . . Mrs Webb?

JOANNA Speaking.

ALAN Alan O'Connell here, *ToyJoys*. Would Simon be around?

JOANNA He's already left, I'm afraid.

ALAN Not to worry, not to worry. How is the lad?

JOANNA Simon? He's . . . fine.

ALAN Grand.

PAUSE IN CONVERSATION – 4 SEC

He'd be quite well, would he?

JOANNA . . . Yes. . . . Is anything wrong?

ALAN No, no. . . . No, let's not say wrong. . . . Would you know where he's gone today, Mrs Webb?

JOANNA He's had to drive my parents to Paddington. Can I take a message? I'm not sure where his calls are later.

ALAN Not to worry. . . . Perhaps he'd like to phone. It's the Area Manager.

JOANNA Of course.

ALAN Grand. . . . Simon is quite well, is he?

JOANNA . . . Yes.

ALAN Grand. . . . Nice speaking, Mrs Webb.

JOANNA . . . Yes.

ALAN . . . Goodbye, now.

JOANNA . . . Goodbye.

CALL 35 – 08.52 – THE SAME DAY

MONA GOODGE:

Hillwater School.

JOANNA WEBB:

(PHONING OUT) . . . Miss Goodge? It's Joanna Webb here. Fern's mother.

MONA Yes, Mrs Webb?

JOANNA Fern's really quite poorly. Something of a tummy upset, I'm afraid. I was going to keep her at home today.

MONA . . . I'm sure that's wise.

JOANNA . . . Miss Goodge . . . I wouldn't mention it,

but . . . Fern doesn't seem to keep things very long.

MONA . . . No?

JOANNA She lost a calculator last week. Then there was a *Walkman*, a sports-bag . . . another *Walkman*, goodness knows what clothes . . .

MONA Anything can move, Mrs Webb.

JOANNA . . . Move?

MONA If it's not screwed to the floor. So many little light-fingers, I fear. We just stick to our golden rule.

JOANNA . . . What would that be?

MONA . . . Screw it to the floor!

JOANNA I see. . . . Fern always gets so upset. Perhaps if I wrote some form of appeal for the school notice-board?

MONA We're not taking anything for the notice-board at present.

JOANNA . . . Oh?

MONA . . . It *moved*.

JOANNA . . . Ah!

MONA Tell Fern to get better soon.

JOANNA . . . Thank you.

MONA . . . Goodbye, Mrs Webb.

CALL 36 – TIMED 10.12 – THE SAME DAY

MRS HENRY (FIRST NAME UNKNOWN): (ANSWERING) Good morning.

BOB PRENTICE:
. . . Uh . . . . . . Mrs Webb?

MRS HENRY Mrs Webb's with the *Oxfam*.

BOB . . . 'Oo's that?

MRS HENRY It's Mrs Webb's daily. I'm here every other day.

BOB . . . Webb there?

MRS HENRY . . . Mr Webb works.

BOB Yeah? Tell 'im it's Bob Prentrice. If 'e . . .

YOU DON'T OPEN THE BOX, MY LITTLE DARLING, YOU GAZE LOVINGLY THROUGH THE CELLOPHANE! . . . Tell Webb, if 'e doesn't get 'is ass up 'ere sharpish, 'e and *ToyJoys* can peddle their trash in 'ell for all . . .

DEAD LINE

CALL 37 – TIMED 12.19 – THE SAME DAY

MRS HENRY:
(ANSWERING) Good morning.
MICHAEL WEBB:
Mrs Henry? It's Michael Webb here. I was hoping to catch Simon.

MRS HENRY Mr Webb's not here, Mr Webb.
MICHAEL . . . Could I leave a message?
MRS HENRY . . . Yes.
MICHAEL Just say, 'A randy little brat shows fun flicks.'
PAUSE IN CONVERSATION – 6 SEC.
MRS HENRY Pardon?
MICHAEL . . . 'A randy little brat shows . . .'
DEAD LINE

CALL 38 – TIMED 13.33 – THE SAME DAY

JOANNA WEBB:
(ANSWERING) Hello, (NUMBER WITHHELD).
SIMON WEBB:
Joanna? This'll have to be quick. I'm way behind and parked on a double-yellow. Any messages?

JOANNA . . . Did mother make the train?
SIMON . . . She had plenty of time for the *next* train. That damned cab might have waited.

JOANNA It waited twenty-five minutes! Mother was in such a state she couldn't find father's inhaler. . . . Why did you have to keep saying that?

SIMON It was a perfectly reasonable thing to say.

JOANNA Reasonable? They'd barely got the car unloaded, when mother was checking the trains back. You must have known she'd fret.

SIMON . . . Any messages?

JOANNA . . . Fern's not well. I'm keeping her at home today.

SIMON Joanna? You're a mug! There's nothing wrong with Fern.

JOANNA . . . She looks dreadful!

SIMON Rubbish! She gets little enough damned schooling when she's there. Joanna, I'm not having Fern picking up Tanya's tricks?

JOANNA . . . Tanya's tricks.

SIMON . . . It's . . . yes. If they don't feel like school, they don't go. Straight back, Joanna, straight back tomorrow!

JOANNA . . . There are some messages.

SIMON . . . Yes?

JOANNA Mrs Henry left a note. She says she wouldn't have stepped in the seed-tray if Bob Prentice hadn't sworn at her, and apparently Michael said something which she . . . uh . . . which she doesn't 'feel beholden to repeat'.

SIMON . . . Helpful!

JOANNA Alan O'Connell wants you to phone . . . and I called in at the garage. Hooper's picking up their car this evening.

SIMON . . . Damned thing! Imagine them leaving that pile of scrap on the doorstep!

JOANNA They didn't have much option. Ronald certainly couldn't drive it back and if you hadn't kept saying . . .

SIMON All right! All right!

JOANNA . . . Simon, we must get that bedside phone

installed. It's madness! The number of times you oversleep and break your neck trying to answer . . .

SIMON If I hadn't taken those bloody tablets . . .

JOANNA Let me get *Telecom* to . . .

SIMON Phones are a doddle! I've said I'll fix it myself and I'll fix it . . . *TWO SECONDS! ONLY JUST DELIVERING! . . . PLEASE . . .*

JOANNA . . . Simon?

SIMON . . . I've already had one ticket today.

JOANNA . . . Simon, we must do something about this leak.

SIMON *I AM MOVING IT!* Given half a chance. *I'M MOVING IT NOW!*

JOANNA I'll drop in and get the Dimmock brothers to have another look at the roof. . . . They said they were always happy to.

SIMON . . . Anyone can have a leak.

JOANNA *Stop* saying that, Simon. Just *stop* saying that.

SIMON . . . *NO! . . . NO! NO! NO!*

JOANNA . . . I'll see you later.

SIMON . . . *FASCIST!*

CALL 39 – TIMED 15.12 – THE SAME DAY

FERN WEBB:
(ANSWERING) Yeah?
SELINA CORK:
Good afternoon. Would that be Mrs Webb?

FERN TOO FAINT TO BE AUDIBLE – 9 SEC.

SELINA . . . I didn't quite catch that.

FERN . . . My name's Fern.

SELINA . . . I do understand . . . Miss Fern.

FERN TOO FAINT TO BE AUDIBLE – 4 SEC.

SELINA Exactly. . . . I'm Selina Cork, phoning on behalf of *Quick-Pane Double-Glazing* and you happen to live in this week's specially selected area, Miss Fern.

FERN . . . Wow!

SELINA *Quick-Pane*'s offering absolutely free estimates to a limited number of carefully chosen clients. May I put you down for a personal feasibility appraisal?

FERN . . . It's all free?

SELINA A free and unrepeatable service, Miss Fern. And always remember, only *Quick-Pane* carries a No-Quibble refund.

FERN . . . D'you do evenings?

SELINA Everthing's arranged to your own individual requirements. That's the *Quick-Pane* way.

FERN He's definitely here Thursday evening. We're having a Neighbourhood Watch meeting.

SELINA Thursday evening? Excellent! . . . You may like to know that *Quick-Pane* do everything to encourage security-consciousness, Miss Fern. Our sister company's *Thief Relief*. May I tick some additional boxes?

FERN . . . Tick some . . . ?

SELINA Neighbourhood Watch Scheme – *Yes*. Do you have any form of domestic alarm?

FERN Not really. . . . I've always wanted a dog.

SELINA *No*. . . . Any external surveillance system?

FERN . . . External . . . ?

SELINA *No*. . . . And have you been burgled within the last two years?

FERN TOO FAINT TO BE AUDIBLE – 6 SEC.

SELINA Could you speak up a little, Miss Fern?

FERN . . . I'm not well today.

SELINA I do sympathize, Miss Fern. Dear, dear, dear! . . . Have you actually had anything stolen?

FERN Sure. . . . I've lost a calculator, two personal stereos, a sports-bag . . .

SELINA Excellent! We should be able to help you here.

FERN . . . Yeah?

SELINA 24, Tufnell Park Terrace, Thursday evening. Shall we say, seven-thirty?

FERN . . . Great!

SELINA I'm sure you'll enjoy the *Quick-Pane Double-Glazing* experience, Miss Fern.

FERN . . . Wow!

SELINA We'll look forward to meeting you and Mr Webb in person. Compliments of *Quick-Pane*.

CALL 40 – TIMED 18.48 – THE SAME DAY

ALAN O'CONNELL:
(NUMBER WITHHELD).
SIMON WEBB:
(PHONING OUT) Alan? Sorry to phone you at home. I just got back.

ALAN Not at all, not at all. Good to hear you.

SIMON . . . Joanna said you called.

ALAN Yes. So I did. . . . Yes.
PAUSE IN CONVERSATION – 5 SEC.
Yes.

SIMON . . . Anything the matter, Alan?

ALAN No, no. Let's not say anything's the matter. . . . Simon, you wouldn't feel in any way now that you've been overdoing things at all? It wouldn't be as though you'd had a holiday . . .

SIMON I'm fine, Alan, I'm fine.

ALAN Grand. . . . You got some rest over the weekend?
PAUSE IN CONVERSATION – 3 SEC.

SIMON I'm fine.

ALAN Grand. . . . I expect you'd like to catch up with some paperwork now. Robin Cudlip says he's still not had the *Talkative Teddies* from his last order, Solomon Lloyd's still lacking the *Cute Newts*, and *Montagues of*

Oxford thank you for expressing the eight dozen *Little Single-Parent Sets*. They've heard they're all safe and sound in Ipswich.

SIMON . . . I'll sort it out.

ALAN . . . Grand.

SIMON . . . Was there anything else?

ALAN No, no. Let's not say there's anything else. . . . Bob Prentice . . .

SIMON I'll sort out Bob Prentice.

ALAN That's grand, Simon. . . . If you could just keep an occasional eye on the paperwork . . .

SIMON Goodbye, Alan.

ALAN . . . Grand.

CALL 41 – TIMED 18.57 – THE SAME DAY

SALLY WIMBUSH:
Hello?

SIMON WEBB:
(PHONING OUT) Sally? . . . Sorry I . . . uh . . . interrupted you the other evening.

SALLY . . . You didn't.

SIMON . . . No . . . . . . I believe Michael phoned.

SALLY I'll find him.

PAUSE IN CONVERSATION – 38 SEC.

MICHAEL WEBB:
Simon?

SIMON Hello, Michael. . . . I've listened to your call.

MICHAEL Right. I checked out Curtis. Curtis Pine wears cufflinks. You want me to leak it to the *Guardian*?

SIMON . . . What sort are they?

MICHAEL Come on! . . . What is this, Simon? You want to wear what the well-dressed man's wearing? You want me to get them copied?

SIMON . . . Michael, are they engraved?

MICHAEL . . . They look . . . yes, they look as though they might be engraved.
SIMON . . . I see.
MICHAEL Simon . . . you're leaving me behind. First, you've got a phantom caller . . .
SIMON He's no phantom.
MICHAEL . . . He's not phoned lately.
SIMON . . . No.
MICHAEL Jack it in, Simon! It's not that big a deal for God's sake! Nutters phone people all the time.
SIMON . . . You haven't got kids, Michael. What if that maniac should get through to Fern? I'd want to nail him.
MICHAEL . . . And the cufflinks?
SIMON . . . It's . . . an idea I'm following up.
MICHAEL . . . Okay. Listen, you've got some pretty sophisticated gear in that basement. If you don't get something soon, we could do with the equipment back, yes?
SIMON . . . Yes.
MICHAEL . . . See you.
SIMON Sure. Bye, Michael.
MICHAEL Bye.

CALL 42 – TIMED 18.57 – THE SAME DAY

BOB PRENTICE:
'Ello?
SIMON WEBB:
(PHONING OUT) Bob? It's Simon Webb, *ToyJoys*.
BOB . . . So it is.
SIMON . . . You'll have the replacements tomorrow.
BOB . . . Want me to piss Champagne?
SIMON . . . Goodbye . . .
BOB 'Oo was that 'ard-nosed bat answered the phone earlier. Proper . . .

SIMON	You'll get your stock.
	DEAD LINE

CALL 43 – TIMED 21.16 – THE SAME DAY

WANDA POOL:
Hi.
KIT WEBB:
(PHONING OUT) Wanda?

WANDA	. . . Hi.
KIT	. . . Yeah.
WANDA	Kit . . . Jason's here. He's just outlining a few theories on Kierkegaard. . . . You want to come round?
KIT	Uh . . . I was just wondering how you were.
WANDA	Well . . . Jason's here.
KIT	. . . Sure.
WANDA	. . . Yeah.
KIT	. . . Some other time then, Wanda.
WANDA	. . . Chaio, now.

CALL 44 – TIMED 23.54 – THE SAME DAY

SIMON WEBB:
(PHONING OUT) . . . can't . . . can't tell you, George . . .
GEORGE MEADOWS:
. . . Si . . . . . . old . . .
PAUSE IN CONVERSATION – 6 SEC.
son . . .

SIMON	. . . can't tell you . . .
GEORGE	. . . can't . . . ?
SIMON	. . . tell you . . .
GEORGE	. . . tell . . .
SIMON	. . . can't . . .

GEORGE . . . tell me . . .
SIMON . . . t'riffic . . . . . . t'riffic night . . .
GEORGE . . . tell me . . .
SIMON . . . t'riffic . . .
GEORGE . . . t'riffic . . .
SIMON . . . can't tell you . . . what . . . t'riffic night . . . had . . .
GEORGE . . . t'riffic . . .
SIMON . . . can't tell you . . .
GEORGE . . . t'riffic . . .
SIMON . . . how much . . . means . . . to . . . able to . . .

PAUSE IN CONVERSATION – 9 SEC.

talk . . .
GEORGE . . . t'riffic . . .
SIMON . . . under . . . stand . . . ?
GEORGE . . . I . . .
SIMON . . . understand . . . ?
GEORGE . . . I . . .
SIMON . . . understand . . . ?
GEORGE . . . understand . . .

PAUSE IN CONVERSATION – 7 SEC.

understand . . .
SIMON . . . J'anna . . .
GEORGE . . . no . . .
SIMON . . . wouldn't have . . .
GEORGE . . . no . . .
SIMON . . . no . . .
GEORGE . . . J'anna . . . wouldn't have . . . ?
SIMON . . . I . . . wouldn't have . . .
GEORGE . . . no . . . ?
SIMON . . . I . . . wouldn't have . . . . . believed it . . .
GEORGE . . . J'anna . . .
SIMON . . . never . . .
GEORGE . . . no . . .
SIMON . . . you . . . under . . . stand . . . ?
GEORGE . . . t'riffic . . .
SIMON . . . means . . . lot . . .
GEORGE . . . mmmm . . .
SIMON . . . twenty . . .

GEORGE . . . mmmm . . .
SIMON . . . twenty . . . years . . .
GEORGE . . . mmmm . . .
SIMON . . . waste . . .
GEORGE . . . t'riffic . . .
SIMON . . . waste . . .
GEORGE . . . t'riffic . . .
SIMON . . . waste . . .
GEORGE . . . mmmm . . .
SIMON . . . J'anna . . . waste . . . waste . . . goose glares at you . . . George . . . ? . . . swastika . . . waste . . . pissing Champagne . . . . . . George . . . ?

PAUSE IN CONVERSATION – 5 SEC.

. . . plants . . . three parking tickets . . . plants everywhere . . . J'anna . . . cufflinks . . . twenty years . . . cufflinks . . . lovingly through the cellophane . . . J'anna . . . notice-boards move . . . cufflinks . . . . . . George . . . ? . . . George . . . ?

PAUSE IN CONVERSATION – 8 SEC.

George . . . ?

PAUSE IN CONVERSATION – 11 SEC.

George . . . ?

PAUSE IN CONVERSATION – 14 SEC.

George . . . ?

TUESDAY 11 MARCH

CALL 45 – TIMED 08.14

NORMAN HOOPER:
All Star Garage.
SIMON WEBB:
(PHONING OUT). Norman? It's Simon Webb.

NORMAN . . . You've landed me!
SIMON How d'you think I feel?
NORMAN What a motor! We've had to push it round the side. One bloke caught sight of it last night and backed into a bollard. He still didn't stop laughing.
SIMON . . . Norman, I'm feeling pretty frail . . .
NORMAN We don't normally have to treat woodworm.
SIMON . . . As long as it can make Ludlow.
NORMAN Ludlow? Do us a favour! How about crossing the Kalahari in your Cortina? This heap's got more rattles than a spoilt child.
SIMON . . . Just get the damned thing moving!
NORMAN All by itself? Oh, dear! Oh, dear!
SIMON . . . Please . . .
NORMAN Say no more. I'll let you have the results of the autopsy.
SIMON . . . Fine.
NORMAN Tell you what. I'll do you a part-exchange on a pair of fluffy dice.
SIMON . . . Bye, Norman.

CALL 46 – TIMED 14.07 – THE SAME DAY

JOANNA WEBB:
(ANSWERING) Hello, (NUMBER WITHHELD).
SIMON WEBB:
Joanna, hello. . . . Get Fern off to school all right?

JOANNA . . . Yes.
SIMON Nothing the matter with her. I told you, Joanna, didn't I tell you?
JOANNA . . . You did.
SIMON She went off quite happily?
JOANNA . . . More or less.
SIMON . . . Good.
JOANNA Simon, she collapsed! . . . Apparently, she turned green and keeled over in assembly. The Goodge lady phoned me at *Oxfam*.
SIMON . . . Oh, God!
JOANNA She's rather rough. Food poisoning. It's hardly surprising, the amount of junk she got through on Sunday.
SIMON . . . Hell!
JOANNA . . . Yes.
SIMON . . . I'm not feeling too good myself.
JOANNA That'll be *alcoholic* poisoning, Simon. Did you have to go out last night?
SIMON It was only a couple of drinks with George.
JOANNA . . . Accountant George? Semi-pro, Country and thingy George?
SIMON . . . Yes.
JOANNA I thought he'd spent a fortune drying-out.
SIMON . . . He did.
JOANNA He wrote a song all about drying-out. It went on forever about the demon drink and . . . 'the beauty of the dry, dry day'.
SIMON . . . Yes.
JOANNA . . . And now he's out getting sloshed.
SIMON . . . The song did rather well.
JOANNA . . . Wonderful!

SIMON And *your* Friday nights at *yoga*? I suppose that's not pure self-indulgence.

JOANNA Frankly, it's just dull. I was desperate for some interest, Simon. I'm not sure sticking a pin in the list of council evening classes was the right way of going about it.

SIMON . . . I said it was lunacy.

JOANNA . . . I did keep my thumb over Advanced Engineering.

SIMON . . . Joanna . . . has Kit left for his interview yet?

JOANNA Yes.

SIMON Damn! I wanted to check he knew where he was going.

JOANNA . . . Why shouldn't he?

SIMON . . . Oh . . . you know Kit. He can be pretty vague. . . . Joanna . . . tell Fern I'm sorry she's bad.

JOANNA *You* tell her.

SIMON . . . Yes.

JOANNA We'll see you later.

SIMON . . . Bye.

CALL 47 – TIMED 17.10 – THE SAME DAY

JOANNA WEBB:

(ANSWERING) Hello, (NUMBER WITHHELD).

CURTIS PINE:

. . . How are you?

JOANNA . . . Fine.

CURTIS . . . Good.

JOANNA . . . It seems ages.

CURTIS . . . Yes. . . . You'll have some time after the class on Friday?

JOANNA . . . Of course.

CURTIS . . . I know it can work, Joanna. I'm sure of it.

JOANNA . . . If you're sure, I'm sure.

CURTIS . . . That's my girl.
JOANNA Curtis . . . my daughter's calling. I'll have to go.
CURTIS . . . Till Friday.
JOANNA . . . Yes.

CALL 48 – TIMED 19.21 – THE SAME DAY

KIT WEBB:
(ANSWERING) *Children's Ward*
WANDA POOL:
Hi, Kit.
KIT Wanda! Hey, I've got a job.
WANDA . . . That's good, Kit. . . . We've been busted.
KIT *Busted?*
WANDA Yeah.
KIT Jeez!
WANDA It was gruesome, Kit! Four police barged in, complete with sniffer. They've wrecked the place. Big Gut hid in the old water tank and the dog was all over everything. It banged its head and went a bit funny.
KIT Did they get Swastika?
WANDA Yeah. He didn't have any stuff on him, but they found it in the first-aid box. They kept shoving things into little plastic-bags.
KIT Yeah?
WANDA Yeah. They've taken the curry powder for analysis.
KIT . . . All of it?
WANDA All of it. Then they couldn't find the dog. Swastika Joe said they'd better report it missing to the police.
KIT Good for Swastika!
WANDA Yeah. They took him straight out to the van. . . . Big Gut gave himself up. The dog had found him in the old water tank and wouldn't stop licking him.

KIT Yeah?

WANDA The sergeant said at least Big Gut was coming clean and they all pissed themselves. It was gruesome!

KIT . . . Well, yeah.

WANDA . . . You've got a job?

KIT Right. You're talking to a waiter. There's a restaurant opening near the Barbican. It's got, like, a Shakespearean theme, Wanda. Yeah. They're calling the place the *As U Like It*.

WANDA . . . Nice one.

KIT Start next week. I'll be helping them get things together till it's open. . . . Jeez! It's bad about the bust.

WANDA . . . It was gruesome!

KIT . . . You want to come round, or something?

WANDA I was going to case the station, check out what's happening.

KIT Right. Hope it comes good, Wanda.

WANDA Sure.

KIT . . . Chaio, now.

WANDA . . . Chaio, now.

CALL 49 – TIMED 19.43 – THE SAME DAY

KIT WEBB:
(ANSWERING) *Terminal Tummy-Upsets*

DUSTIN CAROWAY:
. . . Hello? . . . Is that Kit?

KIT . . . Yeah?

DUSTIN . . . It's Dustin here. We met at the *As U Like It*.

KIT . . . Oh, sure.

DUSTIN Are you taking the job?

KIT . . . Nothing to lose.

DUSTIN That's how I feel. Get in there! D'you think it'll ever be ready in time?

KIT Who knows? Dominic seems pretty confident.

DUSTIN Dominic? What a poser! Ever meet a man and just know he's got mirrors on his bedroom-ceiling?

KIT . . . I'm not sure I have.

DUSTIN Meet Dominic.

KIT . . . Yeah?

DUSTIN Kit . . . fancy that drink?

KIT . . . Sure. . . . Where are you, Dustin?

DUSTIN Anywhere, I've got wheels. What time shall I call?

KIT . . . Whenever. . . . It's a turning just past Tufnell Park . . .

DUSTIN I've got the address. It was down on Dominic's monogrammed clip-board.

KIT . . . You remembered . . . ?

DUSTIN See you in half an hour.

KIT . . . Cheers.

DUSTIN . . . Keep torching.

WEDNESDAY 12 MARCH

CALL 50 – TIMED 08.35

DOROTHY GRISEWOOD:
Hello, (NUMBER WITHHELD).
JOANNA WEBB:
(PHONING OUT) Dorothy? I'm sorry to phone so early. It's Joanna.

DOROTHY . . . I'm just getting Tanya off. Joanna, two seconds.
PAUSE IN CONVERSATION – 4 MIN 52 SEC.
So sorry.

JOANNA Dorothy . . . do say no, but I was wondering if I could ask a favour. Do say no if . . .

DOROTHY Of course, dear. What is it?

JOANNA It's just that I'm rather stuck. Fern's not well and I must see Mrs Henry, if she turns up at all. She left the most extraordinary note on Monday. Dorothy, do say no . . .

DOROTHY What *is* it, dear?

JOANNA . . . Could we swap *Oxfam* mornings? I know it's short notice and do say no if it's not . . .

DOROTHY *No.*

JOANNA . . . No?

DOROTHY No.

JOANNA Really *no*?

DOROTHY I simply can't. We've got the Finnemores coming for dinner.

JOANNA Dinner? It's only . . .

DOROTHY Darling, a *dinner*! And you know the Finnemores.
JOANNA . . . Not very well.
DOROTHY But you're having us all tomorrow evening.
JOANNA . . . Tomorrow?
DOROTHY The Neighbourhood Watch meeting.
JOANNA Oh, God! So it is.
DOROTHY I must say I don't envy you the catering.
JOANNA *Catering*? I'm only . . .
DOROTHY Joanna, must dash. Frank's got the Rover, the Peugeot's being serviced and there's a cab at the door for *Selfridges*. Ghastly isn't it?
JOANNA . . . Yes.
DOROTHY Goodbye, dear.
JOANNA . . . Goodbye.

CALL 51 – TIMED 08.48 – THE SAME DAY

JOANNA WEBB:
(ANSWERING) Hello, (NUMBER WITHHELD).
KATE AGNEW:
Joanna?
JOANNA Mother! I was just trying to phone out! . . . Hello. . . . You got back all right?
KATE . . . Eventually, dear.
JOANNA It was lovely to see you both. Such a pity you had to leave so quickly.
KATE Oh, the *relief*!
JOANNA . . . Mother?
KATE We'd no leaks, dear. Not *one*. I'm afraid Simon had planted a seed of doubt.
JOANNA . . . Yes.
KATE Ronald's shooting-brake, dear.
JOANNA . . . Mother, could I phone you back? I'm desperate to contact . . .
KATE The question is, should we pick it up, or could Simon bring it back?
JOANNA . . . Let me have a think, mother. I'll . . .

KATE There's no need to worry, dear. We decided Simon could bring it back.
JOANNA . . . I see.
KATE . . . Goodbye.
JOANNA . . . Goodbye, mother.

CALL 52 – TIMED 08.57 – THE SAME DAY

VAL JESSOP:
Urcht!
JOANNA WEBB:
(PHONING OUT) Val?
VAL *Eeugh!* . . . Joanna? . . . *Oogph!* . . . Still flat out.
JOANNA Val, I'm so sorry.
VAL . . . Hold on. . . . Fag . . . fag . . .
PAUSE IN CONVERSATION – 8 SEC.
light . . .
PAUSE IN CONVERSATION – 11 SEC.
Awwgh! . . . I was on the daub till four.
JOANNA Oh, Val!
VAL . . . *Post-Nuclear Impressions*. *Oogph!* . . . It's a rather large canvas.
JOANNA . . . Yes. . . . Val?
VAL . . . *Oogph!*
JOANNA . . . It's probably impossible and do say . . . uh . . . I'm promised to *Oxfam* this morning, but I've hit problems. I was wondering if there was any chance of your covering.
VAL . . . *Eeugh!*
JOANNA . . . Val?
VAL . . . D'you think I could?
JOANNA Of course. Geraldine should be there. It's only a question of popping in around ten.
VAL COUGHS – 9 SEC.
JOANNA . . . Hello?
VAL . . . All right.
JOANNA Val, that's wonderful. Bless you.

VAL COUGHS – 14 SEC.
JOANNA . . . Bye.

CALL 53 – TIMED 10.32 – THE SAME DAY

MRS HENRY:
(ANSWERING) Good morning.
ROBIN CUDLIP:
Would M-m-m-Mr Webb be around?

MRS HENRY . . . No.
ROBIN I wonder, could I leave a m-m-m-message? You m-m-m-might tell him Robin Cudlip called.
MRS HENRY . . . Yes, I might.
ROBIN Thank you so m-m-m-much. It's *Wonderland M-m-m-Magic* in Stevenage.
MRS HENRY . . . Fancy.
ROBIN . . . Good m-m-m-morning.

CALL 54 – TIMED 11.17 – THE SAME DAY

MRS HENRY:
(ANSWERING) Good morning.
SIMON WEBB (?):
HEAVY BREATHING – 3 SEC.

MRS HENRY Good morning?
SIMON (?) HEAVY BREATHING – 5 SEC.
MRS HENRY Who's that there?
SIMON (?) HEAVY BREATHING – 7 SEC.
MRS HENRY Who's . . . ?
SIMON (?) VERY HEAVY BREATHING – 4 SEC.
MRS HENRY . . . I'm not going to . . .
SIMON (?) VERY HEAVY BREATHING INDEED – 3 SEC.
MRS HENRY SCREAMS – 8 SEC.
DEAD LINE

CALL 55 – TIMED 14.22 – THE SAME DAY

VAL JESSOP:
Val . . . *Eeugh!* . . . Jessop.
JOANNA WEBB:
(PHONING OUT) Val? How was it?

VAL Yes. . . . I'm not sure I'm cut out for *Oxfam*. . . . *Awwgh!* . . . Dorothy swanned in at mid-day.

JOANNA Dorothy?

VAL Mmmm. I was chatting to a bag-person. Poor sod! He'd only dropped in to get warm. . . . *Eeugh!* . . . Dorothy said the shop couldn't be used as a refuge for that type and . . . *Oogph!* . . . chucked him out.

JOANNA Really?

VAL He just looked so . . . *Urcht!* . . . hungry.

JOANNA . . . I can't think why Dorothy called in.

VAL Checking up on us, heart.

JOANNA Oh, damn the woman! Sorry. One of those mornings. I'd just got back with supplies for the wretched Neighbourhood Watch meeting and Mrs Henry swept out saying that was it.

VAL . . . Why?

JOANNA Heaven knows! She muttered something about filth on the kitchen floor being one thing, but filth on the phone being something else.

VAL . . . *Awwgh!*

JOANNA Val, thanks so much for helping out.

VAL . . . *Oogph!*

JOANNA . . . Bye.

CALL 56 – TIMED 16.54 – THE SAME DAY

JOANNA WEBB:
(ANSWERING) Hello, (NUMBER WITHHELD).

TANYA GRISEWOOD:
Hi, Mrs Webb. How's Fern?

JOANNA Hello, Tanya. She's much better, dear. Having a snooze.

TANYA Great! Tell her that mum's got the tickets and there's one for her.

JOANNA . . . Tickets?

TANYA Yeah. Miles Ton! It's the Birmingham concert.

JOANNA *Birmingham*?

TANYA It's the best! Mum said I deserved a treat for only getting the one bicycle stolen this term. It's the day we break up, Mrs Webb.

PAUSE IN CONVERSATION – 6 SEC.

JOANNA Is your mother there?

TANYA She's having a neck-upwards done at *Face Value*. The Finnemores are coming round. You know the Finnemores?

JOANNA I'm *getting* to know them. . . . Ask your mother to call me, would you?

TANYA Sure.

JOANNA . . . Goodbye, Tanya.

TANYA It's the best!

JOANNA . . . Goodbye.

CALL 57 – TIMED 18.38 – THE SAME DAY

JOANNA WEBB:
(ANSWERING) Hello, (NUMBER WITHHELD).

SOLOMON LLOYD:
Mrs Webb?

JOANNA Yes?

SOLOMON Solomon Lloyd here.

JOANNA Ah! Simon's in his *Think* . . . uh . . . the basement. I'll find him.

PAUSE IN CONVERSATION – 1 MIN 54 SEC.

SIMON WEBB:
Hello, Solomon.

SOLOMON *Cute Newts.*
SIMON . . . Yes?
SOLOMON Listen, man. You said I'd be the only front in Bedford with *Cute Newts*. You promised me that, Simon.
SIMON Right.
SOLOMON Then why's Cudlip got them in *Wonderland Magic*?
SIMON Hell!
SOLOMON You won't stock me with his *Talkative Teddies*. What gives?
SIMON . . . He's always had *Cute Newts* in Stevenage. He must have moved some from his other shop, Solomon. . . . You'll have to sort it out between you.
SOLOMON *What*? You mean, like, *relate*? That rip-off merchant's racist, man! When he opened up here I dropped by to say, well . . . more the merrier. You know what he told me? He told me I'd be out of business before I could, 'b-b-b-boil a m-m-m-missionary!' . . . Would you buy that?
PAUSE IN CONVERSATION – 4 SEC.
SIMON I'm sorry, Solomon. I'll see you both on Friday.
SOLOMON Can't be too soon.
SIMON . . . Bye, then.
SOLOMON . . . *Friday*.

CALL 58 – TIMED 18.52 – THE SAME DAY

ROBIN CUDLIP'S RECORDED ANSWER:
RECORDING OF *GOLLIWOGS' CAKEWALK* STARTS.
Hello and welcome to *Wonderland M-m-m-Magic*. If you'd like to leave a m-m-m-message for the Easter B-b-b-Bunny, just speak after you hear the m-m-m-magic bleep. Here's the m-m-m-magic bleep.

BLEEP.

SIMON WEBB:

(PHONING OUT) Simon Webb returning your call, Robin. . . . Apologies for late delivery. . . . Part order already dispatched Stevenage. Six dozen more *Cute Newts*; two dozen *Little Single-Parent Sets*, complete with back-up kits; two dozen *Talkative Teddies*, plus half dozen each, *Teddyphones*, *Teddyvisions* and *Daily Teddygraphs*. . . . Yes, and give us a call, would you?

CALL 59 – TIMED 19.03 – THE SAME DAY

MICHAEL WEBB:

Hello?

SIMON WEBB:

(PHONING OUT) Michael? . . . Our friend's been in contact.

MICHAEL . . . *Yes*? . . . You spoke to him?

SIMON No, no. He got Mrs Henry.

MICHAEL . . . Any idea who it is?

SIMON . . . Difficult. I'd like you to hear the tape, Michael. It's . . . damned unnerving.

MICHAEL . . . I'll drop around tomorrow evening.

SIMON Right . . . uh . . . no. Neighbourhood Watch meeting.

MICHAEL Saturday afternoon?

SIMON . . . Fine.

MICHAEL . . . Well, well, well.

SIMON . . . See you then.

MICHAEL Bye, Simon.

CALL 60 – TIMED 19.15 – THE SAME DAY

SIMON WEBB:
(ANSWERING) Hello, Simon Webb.
DUSTIN CAROWAY:
Mr Webb? It's Dustin Caroway here.

SIMON . . . Yes?
DUSTIN I came back with Kit last night.
SIMON Of course. . . . *Kit*! . . . It was nice to meet you, Dustin.
DUSTIN Nice to meet Kit's family, Mr Webb.
SIMON . . . *Kit*!
DUSTIN . . . Thanks for telling me all about being a rep.
SIMON . . . Not at all.

PAUSE IN CONVERSATION – 4 SEC.

DUSTIN It was a nice evening.
SIMON Yes.
DUSTIN . . . Yes, it was.
SIMON . . . And you're starting work at this restaurant with Kit next week.
DUSTIN Right.
SIMON . . . Good.
DUSTIN Hope it will be.
SIMON . . . Yes.
DUSTIN Right.
SIMON . . . *Joanna, tell Kit there's a call!*

PAUSE IN CONVERSATION – 6 SEC.

Yes.

DUSTIN . . . Have you ever been a waiter, Mr Webb?
SIMON . . . No.
DUSTIN . . . Nor me.
SIMON . . . No.

PAUSE IN CONVERSATION – 5 SEC.

Kit's never been a waiter either.

DUSTIN No. . . . You really ought to meet my mother, Mr Webb.
SIMON . . . Yes?
DUSTIN She's crazy about house-plants, too.
SIMON . . . Kit's right here, Dustin.

PAUSE IN CONVERSATION – 9 SEC.

KIT WEBB:

	Hi.
DUSTIN	Hi.
KIT	. . . Hi.
DUSTIN	What are you up to?
KIT	Hiding in my room. Dad's got to drive the grans' old estate-car back to Ludlow. That's if it ever moves again. He was rowing with mum, like always.
DUSTIN	As long as it's nothing special. Kit, you want to catch an event tomorrow?
KIT	Great!
DUSTIN	There's a show at the *Dodo Studio* called, 'The Cosmos and More'.
KIT	. . . Yeah?
DUSTIN	I've checked the listings here. . . . It says . . . uh . . . 'Prepare for chutzpah! Brim Chorley shows ultimate courage in ditching the *kitsch 'n sinch* for this symbiosis of sound and laser-like improv. Totality emerges triumphant. Brim's cast, coalescing to one neo-Berkoffian persona, presents theatre: repeat, *theatre*. No jerks, but knee-jerks. Synthesized tones, where pure *baroque* tops coffee-*bar rock*, back a visual time-warp compressing eons. Forget Martha Graham, meet Chorley. *Dodo*'s integrity inches back to the wall as Brim axes the gizmo for the gut-getting. Strip for a ticket!'
	PAUSE IN CONVERSATION – 4 SEC.
KIT	Yeah?
DUSTIN	Pick you up sevenish?
KIT	. . . Fine. . . . Yeah, fine.
DUSTIN	. . . Keep torching.
KIT	. . . Sure.

CALL 61 – TIMED 19.44 – THE SAME DAY

KIT WEBB:
(ANSWERING): The Webb residence.
WANDA POOL:
Kit?

KIT Hi, Wanda. . . . What's the damage?

WANDA Big Gut and Swastika have been charged with possession. They're both out though.

KIT . . . Right.

WANDA They didn't like being locked up much.

KIT . . . No?

WANDA Big Gut says he's right off dogs and Swastika Joe . . . . . . Swastika's saving up to have his swastika removed.

KIT . . . Yeah?

WANDA Yeah. . . . He says he hadn't fully thought through the Nazi connotations.

KIT Hey, he's really getting there. What'll we call him?

WANDA . . . Call who?

KIT Joe with a swastika removed.

WANDA Oh, yeah . . . yeah, I dunno . . . *Joe*?

KIT . . . Doesn't have the same ring to it, Wanda.

WANDA No. . . . It's pretty bleak here, Kit. Could I come round?

KIT Wanda . . . dad's being solid. He's heard about your bust.

WANDA How?

KIT Good question. He's got his nose into everything these days. . . . Once dad starts twitching . . . well . . . I'll have to cool him out.

WANDA . . . Sure.

KIT . . . Big Gut's not going on a diet, is he?

WANDA Doesn't seem like it. Why d'you ask?

KIT . . . No reason.

WANDA . . . You sound good, Kit. You're sounding, like, positive.

KIT Yeah . . . ? . . . yeah, must be the job. Wanda, you know anything about . . . uh . . . Brim Chorley?

WANDA . . . No.

KIT . . . Well . . . I'll drop by sometime.

WANDA . . . Sure.

KIT . . . Right.

WANDA . . . Chaio, now.

KIT . . . Keep torching.

THURSDAY 13 MARCH

CALL 62 – TIMED 10.11

JOANNA WEBB:
(ANSWERING) Hello, (NUMBER WITHHELD).
DOROTHY GRISEWOOD:
Joanna?

JOANNA . . . Dorothy . . . yes . . .
DOROTHY . . . Was there something?
JOANNA . . . Tanya mentioned a concert.
DOROTHY Of course. Isn't it wonderful? London was fully booked, but we managed to find seats in Birmingham.
JOANNA . . . Dorothy, I don't know a thing about it.
DOROTHY No? How frightful! Didn't Fern tell you?
JOANNA . . . *Nobody* told me.
DOROTHY Dreadful! Joanna, there was one thing I wanted to mention. . . . Val Jessop.
JOANNA . . . Val?
DOROTHY Do you really think she's the right person? Dealing with the public? I mean, representing *Oxfam*? Small minded, I'm not. Why shouldn't the woman paint? If Val wants to cover her walls with naked men that's entirely up to her, but is it fair, is it proper, is it right to unleash her on a charitable institution?

PAUSE IN CONVERSATION – 4 SEC.

JOANNA You've got to look very hard to tell they are naked men.

DOROTHY	People do look very hard at them, dear. You'd never believe she worked from live models.
JOANNA	. . . She did marry three of them.
DOROTHY	Joanna, if Val wants to lead life on her own terms, that's fine. I simply ask, must she be quite so . . . *frank*?
JOANNA	Why ever not? . . . Anyway, it's not nudes at the moment. Val seems to have gone rather political.
DOROTHY	Oh, my God!
JOANNA	. . . Dorothy . . . the *concert*!
DOROTHY	Yes.
JOANNA	You really should . . .
DOROTHY	It's been no trouble at all, Joanna. Everything's arranged. I'll be driving Fern and Tanya up and we're staying at the . . .
JOANNA	*Staying*? Dorothy, you *really* . . .
DOROTHY	Don't worry, it's my little treat. After all, you're doing the Neighbourhood Watch tonight.
JOANNA	. . . I'm only throwing some nibbles around.
DOROTHY	*Nibbles*, she calls them!
JOANNA	. . . Yes . . . I do.
DOROTHY	LAUGHS – 6 SEC.
JOANNA	. . . I suppose if you'll be looking after them.
DOROTHY	Wouldn't dream of letting them out of my sight. Can you imagine? Fern and Tanya by themselves at a Miles Ton concert?
JOANNA	. . . Yes.
DOROTHY	Darling, could we talk about it this evening? I've got a plumber coming and I'm not really dressed for it.
JOANNA	. . . Of course.
DOROTHY	. . . Bye.
JOANNA	. . . Goodbye, Dorothy.

CALL 63 – TIMED 10.42 – THE SAME DAY

COOKLINE:
. . . economical, so easy to prepare and suitable as a tempting snack or supper dish. All the family will love your Cabbage Quiche. To serve four, you will need . . .

JOANNA WEBB:
(PHONING OUT) . . . everything times three . . .

COOKLINE . . . ounce plain flour, one ounce margarine, one ounce lard, cold water . . .

JOANNA . . . three ounces . . .

COOKLINE . . . medium sized cabbage, two large eggs, half a pint of double-cream, salt and freshly milled pepper.

JOANNA . . . six eggs . . .

COOKLINE . . . an eight-inch flan-tin. Should . . .

JOANNA Splendid!

COOKLINE . . . flan-tin be half an inch wider or narrower than eight inches, do not worry, as your Cabbage Quiche will simply be shallower or deeper . . .

JOANNA Got it!

DEAD LINE

CALL 64 – TIMED 11.09 – THE SAME DAY

JOANNA WEBB:
(ANSWERING) Hello . . .

PIPS

SIMON WEBB:
Joanna?

JOANNA . . . Hello, Simon.

SIMON I dropped in at the garage. Eight hundred and forty odd quid.

JOANNA *Eight* . . . . . . Simon!

SIMON You'll have to get Ronald to write the cheque. I'm lumbered with driving it back already.

JOANNA . . . I'll speak to mother. Simon, you'll be in good time for the meeting?

SIMON . . . Hell! . . . Yes, I'll have to be.

JOANNA Perhaps we ought to . . . lay on a little something.

SIMON It's only a get-together with the police.

JOANNA . . . And a few drinks, maybe.

SIMON . . . Well, don't go mad.

JOANNA No, no. Just a little something. And I've done a 'Cleaner Required' for the newsagent's window. Heaven knows how we'll cope without Mrs Henry. Whatever possessed her to walk out?

PAUSE IN CONVERSATION – 5 SEC.

SIMON There's something odd about some people.

JOANNA . . . Yes. . . . The Dimmocks are looking at the roof again, dear. I told them it was still problematic.

SIMON I don't think they've ever *mended* a leak in their lives. They just move them somewhere else. The Dimmocks regard our roof as some people regard an index-linked pension.

JOANNA . . . Mmmm. . . . Fern's better. She . . .

SIMON Oh, God!

JOANNA . . . What?

SIMON . . . Nothing, really. . . . Fern's not said anything about double-glazing, has she?

JOANNA *Double-*. . . ?

PIPS

Don't put any more money in, dear. We'll see you later.

SIMON Fine.

JOANNA Simon, have I got it right? The Grisewoods are coming, the couple on the corner, there's us, two police, the Finnemores . . . the . . . Oh! It's everything times four!

DEAD LINE

CALL 65 – TIME 12.16 – THE SAME DAY

SIMON WEBB'S RECORDED ANSWER:
RECORDING OF *SPREAD A LITTLE HAPPINESS* STARTS.
Hello. Sorry there's no one here to answer your call at the moment, but if you'd like to leave a message for Simon Webb, or *ToyJoys, Ltd*, kindly do so after the bleep. Thank you.
BLEEP
ROBIN CUDLIP:
I got your m-m-m-message, Simon. Look forward to receiving the m-m-m-much-needed order. . . . B-b-b-By the way, we m-m-m-must talk about Johnnie. . . . M-m-m-Many thanks.

CALL 66 – TIMED 14.45 – THE SAME DAY

KATE AGNEW:
Ahhh! . . . Ludlow . . . Ahhh! . . . (NUMBER WITHHELD).
JOANNA WEBB:
(PHONING OUT) Mother?
KATE I was . . . Ahhh! . . . in the garden. . . . I'll just get my breath.
JOANNA . . . Of course.
KATE . . . One moment.
PAUSE IN CONVERSATION – 6 SEC.
JOANNA Mother?
PAUSE IN CONVERSATION – 8 SEC.
Mother?
PAUSE IN CONVERSATION – 15 SEC.
Mother.
KATE Ahhh! . . . I was clearing the greenhouse, dear. Ronald looks wistful, but he really can't cope with it. Ahhh! . . . One moment.

PAUSE IN CONVERSATION – 29 SEC.
Ohhh! . . . That's better.

JOANNA . . . Good.

KATE Joanna, I'm just going to dismantle the rose arbour. Could you phone back later?

JOANNA Mother!

KATE . . . Goodbye, dear.

JOANNA . . . Goodbye.

CALL 67 – TIMED 15.09 – THE SAME DAY

JOANNA WEBB:
(ANSWERING) Hello, (NUMBER WITHHELD).

JOHN JOLLEY:
Good afternoon. Mrs Webb?

JOANNA Speaking.

JOHN John Jolley here. *Thief Relief*.

JOANNA . . . Yes?

JOHN Just to confirm that we're looking forward to meeting you this evening.

JOANNA . . . Lovely. . . . Who was it?

JOHN *Thief Relief*.

JOANNA . . . Yes?

JOHN We'll see you at eight.

JOANNA . . . Lovely.

JOHN Nice to speak to you, Mrs Webb.

JOANNA . . . Yes.

JOHN Bye, now.

JOANNA . . . Yes. . . . Goodbye, Mr . . . uh . . .

CALL 68 – TIMED 18.14 – THE SAME DAY

KATE AGNEW:
Ludlow (NUMBER WITHHELD).

JOANNA WEBB:
(PHONING OUT) Hello, mother.

KATE Joanna . . . so sorry about this afternoon. 'Get shot of it all,' I thought. I was in the mood.

JOANNA Quite. . . . Mother, we've had some news on Ronald's car.

KATE Splendid. I see he's been sentenced.

JOANNA . . . I'm sorry?

KATE Simon's brother, dear. Didn't you know? *Five* years. 'No Sanctuary for Satanist!', right across the middle pages. . . . Not something one wants to dwell on, I'd have thought.

JOANNA It's a different man altogether!

KATE No, no. Ronald's got all the press-cuttings. He's keeping a scrap-book for reference.

JOANNA . . . Mother, I've not very long. Simon's had an estimate on the car. He can bring it back, but it is rather . . . expensive.

KATE . . . What isn't? . . . Joanna, did I tell you about the little light?

JOANNA . . . Little light?

KATE Yes, dear. We're getting a rather dinky phone, which lights up. Poor Ronald's far too deaf to hear it any more, but now he'll be able to *see* it ring.

JOANNA . . . Mother, if he's that deaf, how . . . ?

KATE Ronald's thrilled. It's amazing what they can do these days, isn't it?

JOANNA . . . The bill for the repairs . . .

KATE I don't suppose Simon intends visiting him.

JOANNA . . . Visiting . . . ?

KATE His brother.

JOANNA . . . There's no *question* . . .

KATE Good. I really wouldn't dwell on it, dear.

JOANNA . . . No.

KATE . . . Goodbye.

JOANNA . . . Goodbye, mother.

CALL 69 – TIMED 18.52 – THE SAME DAY

ROBIN CUDLIP'S RECORDED ANSWER:
RECORDING OF *GOLLIWOGS' CAKEWALK* STARTS.
Hello and welcome to *Wonderland M-m-m-Magic*. If you'd like to leave a m-m-m-message for the Easter B-b-b-Bunny, just speak after you hear the m-m-m-magic bleep. Here's the m-m-m-magic bleep.
BLEEP

SIMON WEBB:
(PHONING OUT) Simon Webb returning your call, Robin. . . . Are you sure about using that tune? . . . Yes, who the hell's Johnnie? . . . See you.

CALL 70 – TIMED 19.31 – THE SAME DAY

SIMON WEBB:
(ANSWERING) Hello, Simon Webb.

ALAN O'CONNELL:
Simon? It's Alan O'Connell.

SIMON Hello, Alan. . . . Sorry, I'm a bit rushed.
ALAN . . . Paperwork.
SIMON . . . What's up with the paperwork?
ALAN . . . Now, you wouldn't have anything on your mind at the moment, would you, Simon? There wouldn't be any little problem that we don't know about?
SIMON . . . I'm fine. . . . What's the matter with the paperwork?
ALAN Oh, let's not say anything's the matter with it. No, no. We just fed your last month's figures into the computer.
SIMON . . . They didn't come out right?
ALAN Well, we fed them in. Since then nothing's come out right.
SIMON . . . Ah!

ALAN	You wouldn't have been a touch preoccupied . . .
SIMON	Oh, God! . . . *JOANNA? THE POLICE HAVE ARRIVED!* . . . Must go, Alan.
ALAN	. . . *What* . . . ?
	DEAD LINE

CALL 71 – TIMED 20.12 – THE SAME DAY

	JOANNA WEBB:
	(ANSWERING) Hello, (NUMBER WITHHELD).
	TANYA GRISEWOOD:
	It's Tanya, Mrs Webb. Is mum there?
JOANNA	Hello, Tanya. . . . Yes.
TANYA	Could I speak to her?
JOANNA	Uh . . . She might be a moment or two. Your mother's addressing the Neighbourhood Watch meeting. It's quite a speech.
TANYA	A speech! Great! I didn't know she was going to make a speech.
JOANNA	. . . I'm not sure any of us did.
TANYA	What's the speech about?
JOANNA	Law and order, dear. She's explaining some finer points to the police. It's all about the need for vigilance and 'keeping an eagle-eye on the weasels'.
TANYA	Wow! . . . D'you think I could speak to dad?
JOANNA	I'm sure you could. . . . Hold on, dear.
	PAUSE IN CONVERSATION – 18 SEC.
	FRANK GRISEWOOD:
	Hello, Toots.
TANYA	Hi, dad. I hear mum's making a speech.
FRANK	She is that.
TANYA	How's she doing?
FRANK	Not bad. The Finnemores have just applauded. Something about 'keeping an eagle-eye on the weasels'.

TANYA Yeah?

FRANK If your mother has the same effect on the criminal class that she's had on Sergeant Rawle, we're home and dry. His lower lip's trembling.

TANYA Wow! . . . Hey, Dawn wants mum to phone, urgent.

FRANK . . . I'll tell her.

TANYA . . . Could I speak to Fern?

FRANK I think not. Her father's sent her to bed.

TANYA . . . She's just been in bed for two days.

FRANK Mmmm. Someone arrived selling double-glazing and Fern got sent to bed. No explanation forthcoming. . . . Good Lord!

TANYA . . . Dad?

FRANK . . . There's two men at the door dressed up as burglars. . . . They've got striped sweaters with *Thief Relief* written all over them.

TANYA Wow! . . . Sounds like fun!

FRANK Hardly. We'll get back as soon as possible, Toots. Thanks for the message.

TANYA . . . See you.

FRANK . . . Bye, now.

CALL 72 – TIMED 20.39 – THE SAME DAY

DAWN LEES:
Hello?

DOROTHY GRISEWOOD:
(PHONING OUT) Dawn? . . . Dorothy.

DAWN Oh, dear! Is it all right? Can you talk?

DOROTHY Yes . . . I'm in the hall, thank God! It's the only bit of this frightful house that's empty.

DAWN Really? I'd never seen the Webbs as being the hub of society.

DOROTHY You wouldn't now! We're all over salesmen, who seem to think it's market-day.

Constable Pattison's just agreed to install double-glazing. It's the most curious evening. Simon keeps asking the Sergeant about the training of sniffer dogs . . . one simply can't move and the whole place reeks of cabbage . . . *it's utterly delightful*!

DAWN . . . Sorry?

DOROTHY *Such a success! Lovely to see so many old friends.*

DAWN . . . Dorothy?

DOROTHY *Can I help at all, Joanna? . . . My, that looks scrummy! What a feast!*

PAUSE IN CONVERSATION – 8 SEC.

Sorry, darling. Joanna was just negotiating a trolley. God! She's serving some sort of fungus!

DAWN Heavens!

DOROTHY At least Simon had the sense to go out for more wine. . . . Dawn, I must rescue Frank. Two little men have got him intrigued with a burglar-alarm.

DAWN Yes . . . uh . . . Dorothy . . . Sebastian phoned.

DOROTHY . . . Yes?

DAWN There's a message.

DOROTHY Yes, yes?

DAWN . . . He said he can't make Birmingham.

PAUSE IN CONVERSATION – 6 SEC.

DOROTHY He *can't* make Birmingham?

DAWN . . . No.

DOROTHY . . . Bastard!

DAWN . . . Yes.

DOROTHY Bloody little toad!

DAWN Yes.

DOROTHY . . . Bastard!

DAWN Yes.

DOROTHY Doesn't he realize what he's doing to me?

DAWN He is . . . *young*, Dorothy.

DOROTHY . . . Yes. . . . Bastard!

PAUSE IN CONVERSATION – 5 SEC.

Bastard!

DAWN . . . Yes.

DOROTHY I've had it, Dawn. The hotel's already

booked and I'm lumbered with the Webb brat into the bargain. It's far too late for me to back . . . . . . *Absolutely splendid! And such a service to the community* . . . . . . AWWCH!

PAUSE IN CONVERSATION – 7 SEC.

Not at all, Joanna. . . . Yes, it might wash off . . . . . . No, no. I can never steer them either.

BURGLAR-ALARM GOES OFF – 8 SEC.

DAWN *DOROTHY?*

BURGLAR-ALARM CONTINUES – 2 MIN 21 SEC

SILENCE – 6 SEC.

Dorothy?

DOROTHY . . . Ohhh . . .

DAWN . . . What the hell's happening?

DOROTHY . . . Dawn. . . ? . . . Ahhh . . . . . . Another battalion of police have just rushed in . . . . . . I'll have to . . .

DEAD LINE

CALL 73 – TIMED 23.28 – THE SAME DAY

SIMON WEBB:
(ANSWERING) . . . whah . . . ?

KIT WEBB:
. . . Dad?

SIMON . . . son . . .

KIT . . . How was the meeting?

SIMON . . . ohhh . . . kay . . .

KIT Yeah? . . . Listen, I'm still in Kilburn. I'll be staying over with Dustin tonight.

SIMON . . . whah . . . ?

KIT . . . I'm staying with Dustin tonight, dad.

SIMON . . . ohhh . . .

KIT Dad, are you all right?

SIMON . . . kay . . .

PAUSE IN CONVERSATION – 4 SEC.

KIT See you, then.

SIMON . . . ohhhhhhh . . .

DEAD LINE

FRIDAY 14 MARCH

CALL 74 – TIMED – 09.36

JOANNA WEBB:
(ANSWERING) Hello?
UNKNOWN GIRL:
Yes. . . . Mrs Webb? . . . I've seen the ad.

JOANNA . . . Ad?

GIRL 'Pleasant family home – Three mornings a week – Light cleaning.'

JOANNA Oh, yes. . . . Could you hold on a minute? I'm afraid we had a bit of a party last night. . . . I was just getting the quiche out of the carpet, but the leak seems to have found some wiring and the vacuum's packed up. One moment, I'll have to ask the men on the roof . . .

DEAD LINE

Oh!

CALL 75 – TIMED 11.49 – THE SAME DAY

JOANNA WEBB:
(ANSWERING) Hello?
KIT WEBB:
Hi, mum. Dad sounded pretty tanked up last night. How was the Neighbourhood Watch?

JOANNA I'm not entirely sure, dear. Someone demonstrated a burglar-alarm, yet more police arrived . . . Dorothy went home in floods, no one ate any quiche and your father's agreed to install double-glazing.

KIT . . . No wonder he hit the bottle.

JOANNA Yes. . . . I'm putting official 'Burglar Beware!' stickers in the windows. Your father's decided to spend the day in bed.

KIT . . . He's getting paranoid.

JOANNA He's certainly ordered enough security equipment. I must say the alarm sounded very impressive. If only there hadn't been a police car passing.

KIT . . . Sounds more exciting than the *Dodo Studio*.

JOANNA . . . But you said the show had to be . . . uh . . . 'the ultimate'.

KIT Yeah. . . . We left in the interval.

JOANNA That bad?

KIT It was that bad we thought it had finished. Brim Chorley's something else. An hour and a half of nothing and it's still not over. People were actually going back in for more nothing.

JOANNA . . . Oh!

KIT That guy who reviewed it's an artist.

JOANNA . . . It's nice that you could stay with Dustin.

KIT . . . Yeah. . . . He's got a great flat. . . . Yeah. . . . Listen, we're checking out an exhibition. See you later.

JOANNA . . . Go carefully.

CALL 76 – TIMED 12.18 – THE SAME DAY

JOANNA WEBB:
(ANSWERING) Hello?

CURTIS PINE:
. . . Joanna?

JOANNA . . . Curtis . . .

CURTIS . . . Yes.

JOANNA . . . Curtis . . . tonight may be difficult. . . . It's the first day I've got Fern back to school, the kitchen's in chaos and Simon's still in bed groaning. We had a Neighbourhood Watch meeting last night and you'd think the house had been ransacked. . . . I'm not sure I'll make the yoga class.

CURTIS . . . Joanna . . . you *must*! You absolutely *must*!

JOANNA . . . If I *can't* . . .

CURTIS You know what this means to me, Joanna.

JOANNA . . . Yes.

CURTIS It's essential I talk to you . . . tonight.

JOANNA . . . I see.

CURTIS . . . Please.

JOANNA . . . All right.

CURTIS Good girl. . . . You've not mentioned anything to Simon?

JOANNA Of course not.

CURTIS No. . . . Sorry. I'm always so worried about word getting back. . . . Joanna, I was just phoning to say I've got a meeting, so not to worry if I don't make the yoga myself. I'll meet you there afterwards.

JOANNA Curtis! . . . *Fern*? . . . *Why've you come home*?

CURTIS . . . See you later.

CALL 77 – TIMED 12.25 – THE SAME DAY

JOANNA WEBB:
(ANSWERING) Hello?

UNKNOWN MAN FROM *BIG CLEAN-UP*:
Mrs Webb?

JOANNA . . . Yes?

MAN It's regarding your advertisement for part-time help. I represent *Big Clean-Up* and we might be able to assist you.

JOANNA . . . You're an agency?

MAN Exactly. If you'd let me have a few extra details I'm sure we could sort you out. . . . Would there be any weekend cleaning involved?

JOANNA No, none at all.

MAN . . . How about interviews? Would you be free to meet hopeful employees . . . uh . . . this weekend for example?

JOANNA We could tomorrow. Sunday, we're away all day.

MAN I see. No one there on Sunday.

JOANNA . . . No.

MAN Well, I'm sure you'll be hearing from us, Mrs Webb.

JOANNA . . . And you were?

MAN *Big Clean-Up*. You can rely on us.

JOANNA . . . Splendid.

MAN . . . Goodbye, Mrs Webb.

JOANNA . . . Goodbye.

CALL 78 – TIMED 14.08 – THE SAME DAY

SIMON WEBB'S RECORDED ANSWER:

RECORDING OF *SPREAD A LITTLE HAPPINESS* STARTS.

Hello. Sorry there's no one here to answer your call at the moment, but if you'd like to leave a message for Simon Webb, or *ToyJoys, Ltd*, kindly do so after the bleep. Thank you.

BLEEP

ROBIN CUDLIP:

I got your m-m-m-message, Simon. What do you m-m-m-mean, who's Johnnie? . . .

Johnnie b-b-b-bloody Foreigner! . . . Yes, and I've still not received last m-m-m-month's order.

CALL 79 – TIMED 16.52 – THE SAME DAY

FERN WEBB:
(ANSWERING) Yeah?
TANYA GRISEWOOD:
Hi, Fern. I'm sorry you got sent home from school early.

FERN It's just not fair, Tanya! Dad sent me to bed last night for letting the double-glazing people call.

TANYA Yeah?

FERN Then they made so much noise, I couldn't sleep. I felt really bad about nodding off in Home Economics.

TANYA Sure.

FERN So I get sent home for nodding off, but dad's been in bed all day and mum says he's bought the double-glazing. . . . If there's one class I ought to stay awake in, it's Home Economics.

TANYA What happened last night? My mum came home and screamed at me.

FERN What d'you do?

TANYA Nothing. I just said that Birmingham was going to be great. Then she screamed at me.

FERN Yeah?

TANYA She was in some mood, Fern. She sat down and wrote to the Chief Constable complaining that Sergeant Rawle had used an obscene word in public.

FERN . . . Which word?

TANYA I dunno. Mum says a lot of burglar-alarms went off, a carload of more police rushed in and Sergeant Rawle went too far.

FERN Wow!

TANYA She liked Constable Pattison though. . . . Dad says your whole household's loopy. Can I come round?

FERN Better not. Mum says I've got to help clear up, or she won't be in time for her yoga. It's just not fair!

TANYA Yeah. Only twelve days to the concert, Fern!

FERN Yeah! Twelve days!

TANYA . . . Bye.

CALL 80 – TIMED 20.17 – THE SAME DAY

KIT WEBB:
(ANSWERING) *Fort Knox.*

GEORGE MEADOWS:
. . . That's . . .?

KIT . . . Kit.

GEORGE Sure it's Kit. Whahay! George Meadows, Kit. How you doing?

KIT . . . Hi, Mr Meadows. . . . I've got a job.

GEORGE Stick with it, Kit! You wanna know about *graft*? I'll tell you . . .

KIT Dad's right here, Mr Meadows.

PAUSE IN CONVERSATION – 2 MIN 41 SEC.

SIMON WEBB:
George?

GEORGE Si, old son? Tomorrow night, get your ass down here.

SIMON . . . What is it, George?

GEORGE As of now, Si, you're an honorary member of the S.T.E.W.S.

SIMON . . . The S . . . ?

GEORGE The *Stuff the Ex-Wife Society*. LAUGHS – 8 SEC. Just formed it. You're speaking to the president.

SIMON . . . But, George, I'm . . .

GEORGE No buts, Si. First meeting tomorrow night.

We've got Larry, Guy, Andy . . . uh . . . Andy . . . Rick . . . Wayne . . .

SIMON . . . *Wayne*? . . . He's splitting with Lois?

GEORGE He'd had enough, Si. Divorce'll be through any moment. . . . Cruelty.

SIMON Wayne proved mental cruelty?

GEORGE Forget mental! Things got so rough, Wayne had his doc photograph the bruises.

SIMON . . . You're kidding.

GEORGE Ask Wayne to show you the snaps. They came out pretty well.

SIMON God!

GEORGE He always carries them round. . . . Whahay! My place tomorrow, eight sharp!

SIMON . . . George . . . I know I said . . .
TOO FAINT TO BE AUDIBLE – 9 SEC.

GEORGE Turn the amps up, Si.

SIMON TOO FAINT TO BE AUDIBLE – 14 SEC.

GEORGE I'm still not tuning. . . . You said it was only a matter of time.

SIMON . . . I don't have . . . proof.

GEORGE Point taken. We'll make you a junior member.

SIMON . . . Okay.

GEORGE That's my Si. . . . I spoke to your . . . Kit. He said he'd found a job.

SIMON Yes. . . . He seems to be making a few decent friends too.

GEORGE Time solves the lot, Si.

SIMON . . . See you tomorrow.

GEORGE Whahay!

SIMON . . . Cheers, George.

CALL 81 – TIMED 20.48 – THE SAME DAY

KIT WEBB:

(ANSWERING) The Webb residence.

DUSTIN CAROWAY:
Kit?

KIT . . . Hello.
DUSTIN . . . Hello.
KIT How are you?
DUSTIN Fine.
KIT . . . Good.
DUSTIN You?
KIT . . . It's the first day of forever.

PAUSE IN CONVERSATION – 7 SEC.

DUSTIN What are you up to?
KIT Not much. Dad's being a pain.
DUSTIN . . . Yeah?
KIT He spends most of the day in bed, then wears out the carpet trying to remember what he's not done. He's just gone to ground in his *Think Tank.*
DUSTIN . . . Some guy.
KIT One good thing. He said he likes you.
DUSTIN Yeah? Well, I'm a pretty likeable person.
KIT . . . I never noticed.
DUSTIN . . . Kit, it's better if I do go back and see the parents this weekend, before we start work.
KIT Right. Mum's insisting we all have a day out on Sunday anyway. It's a drag. She says dad needs a break. All day in bed and he needs a break? It's getting a drag.
DUSTIN Sure.
KIT . . . I'll see you Monday.
DUSTIN . . . Great.

PAUSE IN CONVERSATION – 5 SEC.

Kit . . . . . . I love you.

PAUSE IN CONVERSATION – 8 SEC.

Kit?

KIT . . . Yeah. . . . Ditto.

PAUSE IN CONVERSATION – 12 SEC.

DUSTIN Yeah.
KIT . . . Goodnight, Dustin.
DUSTIN . . . Goodnight, Kit.

SATURDAY 15 MARCH

CALL 82 – TIMED 10.31

SOLOMON LLOYD:
Hello, *Kids Korner*.
SIMON WEBB:
(PHONING OUT) Solomon . . . sorry I couldn't make it yesterday. Major headache. Got stuck in London.

SOLOMON Listen, man, get Cudlip sorted!
SIMON . . . I've tried to get him . . .
SOLOMON Will you buy this? He walked in here earlier, right into the shop, man . . . looks round the place like it's a porno-front, tells me he's doing a bomb in *Cute Newts* and goes out whistling *Mammy*! . . . Fix it, Simon!
SIMON . . . I'll be there, Monday.
SOLOMON Better way, man.
SIMON . . . Monday morning.
SOLOMON Make it!

CALL 83– TIMED 10.54 – THE SAME DAY

JOANNA WEBB:
(ANSWERING) Hello . . .
PIPS

SHARON DUKES:
Hello? Hello, is that the cleaning? . . . I was calling about the cleaning.

JOANNA . . . I see.
SHARON It's Sharon. . . . Sharon Dukes. I do clean.
JOANNA . . . Were you from the agency, Sharon?
SHARON . . . I spotted you in the window.
JOANNA . . . Yes.
SHARON 'Pleasant family home . . .' . . . It was something like that I was looking for.
JOANNA . . . Lovely.
SHARON . . . Yes.
JOANNA Would you be able to start on Wednesday?
SHARON . . . I could start on Wednesday.
JOANNA . . . Well, if you'd like to come around nine, Sharon, we'll see how it goes, shall we?
SHARON . . . Let's see how it goes.
JOANNA . . . Yes.
SHARON I'll come around nine on Wednesday.
JOANNA . . . Lovely.
SHARON . . . Bye.
JOANNA . . . Goodbye . . . Sharon.

CALL 84 – TIMED 11.12 – THE SAME DAY

FERN WEBB:
(PHONING OUT) . . . *why we have to spring-clean before the cleaner arrives?*
***HITLINE*:**
. . . cuppa tea –
She's my cuppa tea,
And I need a cuppa up, cuppa up –
But her cuppa tea,
It just isn't me,
And she never wants another cuppa up.
Cuppa up, cuppa up, cuppa up, up, up –
Cuppa up, cuppa up, cuppa up!
Cuppa up, cuppa up, cuppa up, up, up –

Cuppa up, cuppa up, cuppa up!'
JINGLE – 12 SEC.
MIKE MARSH:
Hi, there. This is Mike Marsh and you're holding on to the *Hitline*. Hang in there! And it's a big hello to Betty Croyd from all the family. They say congratulations on passing the exam and you're hoping to make a career in the advertising world. Get well soon, Betty. . . . Coming up for you and the host of *Hitline* groupies, it's Trev and Stan with *My Cuppa Tea*.
INSTRUMENTAL – 8 SEC.
TREV AND STAN:
'She's my cuppa tea –
Yes, my cuppa tea,
And I need a cuppa up, cuppa up –
She's my cuppa tea –
Not your cuppa tea,
And I want to sup another cuppa up.
Cuppa up, cuppa up, cuppa up!
It's a big fat pot,
But it's still quite hot,
And I really need another cuppa up –
Why d'ya call me pissed
And a chau-vin-ist,
When I only want another cuppa up?
Cuppa up, cuppa up, cuppa up, up, up –
Cuppa up, cuppa up, cuppa up!
Cuppa up, cuppa up . . .'
DEAD LINE

CALL 85 – TIMED 14.23 – THE SAME DAY

VAL JESSOP:
COUGHS – 7 SEC.
JOANNA WEBB:
(PHONING OUT) Val?

VAL . . . *Oogph!*
JOANNA . . . Val? How are you?
VAL *Eeugh! . . . Urcht!* . . . Fine.
JOANNA . . . Oh, good.
VAL Ploughing on with the *Post-Nuclear Impressions*.
JOANNA . . . How's it going?
VAL Not bad. Rather pleased with the weeping politicians. Somewhat innovatory! . . . I'm just getting stuck into a decomposing civil-servant. *Awwgh*! Still can't get the sky right. . . . Holocausts do present problems.
JOANNA . . . Yes.
VAL . . . I'm not sure how to deal with a post-nuclear social-worker. I suppose they'd feel rather let down.
JOANNA . . . Probably.
VAL *Eeugh*! . . . You sound a touch iffy, heart.
JOANNA . . . Just a bit. Everyone's out . . . except Simon. He's upstairs wiring the extension phone at last. I suppose that's one thing. . . . Val . . . I'm not sure what to do . . . he's becoming so . . . obsessive.
VAL . . . Simon?
JOANNA . . . Yes. . . . He seems on a different plane most of the time. . . . I can't get any sense out of him. Yesterday, I mentioned that Fern was going to a Miles Ton concert and he asked if he was the singer with dimples in his bum.
VAL . . . *Oogph*!
JOANNA . . . Yes. . . . Michael says there's nothing to worry about, but this vagueness . . . it's so unlike him.
VAL . . . Want to pop around?
JOANNA . . . That would be . . .
INTERFERENCE ON LINE – 9 SEC.
VAL . . . Joanna?
JOANNA . . . Yes?
VAL . . . You could give my canvas the once . . .
INTERFERENCE ON LINE – 17 SEC.

JOANNA . . . Hello? Val?

VAL . . . Still here.

JOANNA . . . I'll come right . . .

INTERFERENCE ON LINE – 4 SEC.

DEAD LINE

LINE OUT OF ORDER

SUNDAY 16 MARCH

LINE OUT OF ORDER

MONDAY 17 MARCH

CALL 86 – TIMED 20.12

SALLY WIMBUSH:
Hello?
MICHAEL WEBB:
(PHONING OUT) Just testing! . . . Hello, Sally.

SALLY Where the hell have you been?
MICHAEL Hold hard, love. I've had to sort out Simon's phone. He'd bodged it completely.
SALLY But it's gone eight.
MICHAEL . . . There's been an additional problem.
SALLY Oh, yes?
MICHAEL Simon's been burgled.
SALLY *Burgled*? . . . What? Really burgled?
MICHAEL Really burgled.
SALLY . . . Christ!
MICHAEL It's chaos! Everything seems to have gone . . . except the plants.
SALLY . . . How on earth . . . ?
MICHAEL Must have been yesterday. Joanna arranged a day out to take Simon's mind off things.
SALLY Wonderful!
MICHAEL Anyway, I've got their damned bedside phone installed. It's just a pity there's no bed.
SALLY . . . I've had the most strange sensation.
MICHAEL What would that be?
SALLY Sympathy for Simon.
MICHAEL Right. I'm coming straight back. They seem

more or less organized. Fern and Kit are being farmed out and Simon's dug a load of camping gear out of the attic.

SALLY Poor loves!

MICHAEL Open a bottle. I'll be right home.

SALLY . . . See you.

MICHAEL Cheers.

CALL 87 – TIMED 20.38 – THE SAME DAY

SOLOMON LLOYD:
Bedford (NUMBER WITHHELD).

SIMON WEBB:
(PHONING OUT) Solomon, what can I say? We got back last night, the house had been emptied. Hell! The sods didn't even leave us with a mess. You can imagine what today's been like.

SOLOMON . . . Yes, sure can.

SIMON Talk about a knock!

SOLOMON . . . No sweat.

SIMON I'm really sorry I couldn't get to you.

SOLOMON Don't worry, man. Everything's sweet.

PAUSE IN CONVERSATION – 4 SEC.

SIMON That's . . . good of you, Solomon.

SOLOMON Not at all.

SIMON I knew you'd understand.

SOLOMON No problem. By the by, thanks for the *Talkative Teddies*.

SIMON . . . *What*?

SOLOMON Got 'em this morning.

SIMON Solomon! . . . That's not your order! How can . . . ?

SOLOMON They look good, Simon, real good.

SIMON . . . That's Cudlip's stock! You can't have . . .

SOLOMON Can't I? . . . Hang on there.

PAUSE IN CONVERSATION – 9 SEC.

TALKATIVE TEDDY:
Hello. I'm *Talkative Teddy*. I really, really like talking to you. Fun, isn't it? I really, really like talking to you.

SIMON . . . *Solomon*!
SOLOMON LAUGHS – 11 SEC.
DEAD LINE

CALL 88 – TIMED 20.52 – THE SAME DAY

VAL JESSOP:
Urcht! Val . . . *Oogph*! . . . Jessop.
JOANNA WEBB:
(PHONING OUT) Val?

VAL Hello, heart.
JOANNA How are things? Fern settled down?
VAL Oh, yes. We were going to watch *A Hiccup in the Blood Bath*, but decided not to.
JOANNA I do think that's wise, Val. Simon's rather . . .
VAL Yes. Fern said she'd seen it at Georgina's. *Eeucht*! She's watching *Another Hiccup in the Blood Bath*.
JOANNA . . . Ah!
VAL Want a word?
JOANNA Please, Val.
PAUSE IN CONVERSATION – 18 SEC.

FERN WEBB:
Hi, mum.

JOANNA Fern, dear. Everything all right?
FERN Smashing! Yeah! Val wants me to model for her. She says I'm the perfect image for *Post-Nuclear Pubescence*. I get to wear rags. It's the best!
JOANNA . . . As long as you're not missing home.
FERN Oh, no. I'm in a great room. It's got an exercise-bike, a home-brewery, and there's a load of pictures, but I can't make out what they are. Val's smashing!

JOANNA	. . . That's lovely, dear. As long as you're not . . .
FERN	Goodnight, mum.
JOANNA	. . . Yes, dear. . . . Goodnight.

CALL 89 – TIMED 21.11 – THE SAME DAY

GEORGE MEADOWS:
Redhill (NUMBER WITHHELD).
SIMON WEBB:
(PHONING OUT) George? It's Simon.

GEORGE	Whahay! Hi, Si. What a night, eh? Long live the *STEWS*.
SIMON	Yes.
GEORGE	Joanna understand that we couldn't let you drive home Saturday night? Remember Rick with the hose-pipe? LAUGHS – 6 SEC. Remember Andy throwing the slates down?
SIMON	. . . Yes.
GEORGE	How was your family outing? You got back in time? Your lady sorted? Your mind settled?
SIMON	We got burgled.
GEORGE	. . . *What*?
SIMON	Burgled. They've taken the lot.
GEORGE	. . . You're kidding me.
SIMON	George, you know anything about insurance?
GEORGE	Insurance? Yeah. You keep paying for something you hope and pray won't happen, so that if it does happen you can start paying even more for it not to happen again.
SIMON	. . . Even so . . .
GEORGE	Sure. If you've lost enough, perhaps it's jackpot time.
SIMON	I'm seeing the bank tomorrow. They'll have

to keep cashing the cheques till *Clover Cover* comes through. I was wondering how long it takes.

GEORGE Keep at 'em, Si. Listen, you need any help, we'll all rally. You wanna know about *friends*, Si? Saturday week's STEW's night, yes?

SIMON . . . Fine.

GEORGE Whahay!

SIMON . . . Cheers, George.

CALL 90 – TIMED 21.46 – THE SAME DAY

JOANNA WEBB:
(ANSWERING) Hello, (NUMBER WITHHELD).

KIT WEBB:
Hi, mum. How you doing?

JOANNA Oh, Kit! It's horrid! All the marks are showing where things used to be. They've been merciless! If only we hadn't had brass bedsteads . . . and the cooker, Kit! Why the cooker?

KIT You kept saying you wanted to change it.

JOANNA Not for a *Primus*! Thank God, Michael's got the phone working. Your father's been running to the one on the corner all day. He's cancelled the burglar-alarms.

KIT That figures.

JOANNA . . . And the double-glazing. Constable Pattison says he's cancelled his double-glazing too.

KIT . . . Are the police getting anywhere?

JOANNA In a way. They've been around all the neighbours. Apparently, the Finnemores saw three men arrive with a furniture van. Mrs Finnemore asked what was happening and they said they were bailiffs with a repossession order on everything.

KIT . . . What did Mrs Finnemore do?
JOANNA She said she wasn't surprised.
KIT Jeez!
JOANNA Sergeant Rawle did say he'd known more efficient Neighbourhood Watch schemes. They even took the 'Burglar Beware!' stickers.
KIT . . . What a bloody mess!
JOANNA Oh, Kit! Kit, darling, how was the first day at work?
KIT Yeah, it's good.
JOANNA I am glad.
KIT The *As U Like It*'s going to be a really plushy number. It's got . . .
JOANNA Hold on, Kit. Your father's just . . . Oh, it's all right. He's stretched out on the lino. . . . What was that?
KIT . . . It's a nice job.
JOANNA Lovely. I am sorry you've got to stay with Dustin. Will he mind very much?
KIT . . . Uh . . . Dustin's . . . pretty accommodating.
JOANNA Yes, we all liked him.
KIT . . . Yeah?
JOANNA Well, take care, dear. Lots of love to Dustin.
KIT . . . Sure.
JOANNA Goodnight, Kit.
KIT Bye, mum.

TUESDAY 18 MARCH

CALL 91 – TIMED 09.07

SIMON WEBB:
(ANSWERING) Hello, Simon Webb.
ALAN O'CONNELL:
Alan O'Connell, Simon . . . And how would you be?

SIMON . . . Fine, Alan . . . I'm fine.
ALAN Good, good. Solomon Lloyd and . . . uh . . . Robin Cudlip.
SIMON . . . Yes?
ALAN Would I be right in thinking that it's not a relationship plagued by excessive generosity?
SIMON You've heard from them?
ALAN Robin did happen to call, so I called Solomon, who suggested I call you. Now I'm not suggesting for one moment that there's a problem here, Simon, but . . . uh . . . what's the problem?
SIMON Well . . . Robin's got *Cute Newts* in Stevenage.
ALAN . . . Yes?
SIMON Robin then transfers some to Bedford. Bedford's all Solomon's for *Cute Newts*. Robin can't stand Solomon for reasons best known to himself, and Solomon can't stand Robin because he's got *Cute Newts*.
ALAN . . . If Robin's got . . .

SIMON He has. He's also got *Talkative Teddies* in Bedford. I misrouted an order and Solomon gets the *Talkative Teddies*. Right? *Talkative Teddies* and *Cute Newts*!

ALAN . . . *Talkative Teddies* . . .

SIMON *Achhht*!

ALAN . . . Simon?

SIMON Sorry, Alan. Cramp. *Achhht*! . . . I'm sitting on the floor. . . . *It's all right, Joanna. Just take that damned goose out of here*! . . . Alan?

ALAN . . . Simon, are you all right?

SIMON . . . Perfectly all right.

ALAN It's just that I'll have to explain to Sales . . .

SIMON *Oocht*! . . . *Joanna, if that's the police again* . . . *Eeecht*! . . . Must go, Alan. Bye.

ALAN . . . Simon . . . ?

DEAD LINE

CALL 92 – TIMED 10.56 – THE SAME DAY

SWITCHBOARD GIRL AT *COMPUTRON*:
Hello, *Computron International*. Could you hold the line, please?

JOANNA WEBB:
(PHONING OUT) Of course.

PAUSE IN CONVERSATION – 52 SEC.

GIRL Hello, *Computron International*. Can I help you?

JOANNA Would Michael Webb be available?

GIRL Who's speaking?

JOANNA It's Joanna Webb.

GIRL . . . Your husband has someone with him, Mrs Webb, but I will check.

JOANNA Thank you. Actually, he's not my . . .

RECORDING OF *RAVEL'S BOLERO* STARTS – 14 SEC.

Hell's bloody teeth!

RECORDING OF *RAVEL'S BOLERO* CONTINUES – 1 MIN 42 SEC.

GIRL Mr Webb's available now.

PAUSE IN CONVERSATION – 7 SEC.

MICHAEL WEBB:
Hello?

JOANNA Michael? It's Joanna.

MICHAEL Hello, love. I've fixed up a *Computron* van. You can pick it up first thing tomorrow.

JOANNA That's wonderful. We've heaven knows what to collect. It's like starting from scratch . . . Michael . . . ?

MICHAEL . . . Yes?

JOANNA Simon.

MICHAEL . . . Yes?

JOANNA He's looking quite haunted.

MICHAEL . . . It's hardly surprising. Even without the burglary . . .

JOANNA It's more than that, Michael. He's barely talking to anyone. He won't take a break, he won't go back to that doctor, and if he doesn't do something he's heading for a full-scale crack-up. It's so unlike him.

MICHAEL . . . Joanna, trust me. . . . Simon's got a lot on his mind.

JOANNA He's always coped before. Surely you could talk to him?

MICHAEL . . . Yes.

JOANNA Please, Michael. No one else can. He's spending most of his time in the basement. Last night he came up, dropped to his knees and . . .

MICHAEL Joanna, don't . . . uh . . . I must go.

JOANNA Michael!

MICHAEL I'll have a word with him. All right?

JOANNA . . . Yes.

MICHAEL Try not to worry. Bye, then.

JOANNA . . . Goodbye, Michael.

CALL 93 – TIMED 11.14 – THE SAME DAY

JOANNA WEBB:
(ANSWERING) Hello, (NUMBER WITHHELD).
CURTIS PINE:
Joanna? I was trying to phone all weekend.

JOANNA	Curtis . . .
CURTIS	Your coat got left in the car.
JOANNA	You've got . . . Oh, Curtis . . .
CURTIS	. . . Joanna?
JOANNA	SOBS – 7 SEC.
CURTIS	Whatever's up? It's only a coat.
JOANNA	SOBS – 11 SEC.
CURTIS	Hey, there . . .
JOANNA	Curtis . . . we've lost everything. They took everything, but you've got my . . . SOBS – 4 SEC. We were burgled.
CURTIS	. . . You poor thing.
JOANNA	. . . I'm sorry, Curtis. I'm so sorry.
CURTIS	Is anyone there with you?
JOANNA	No. . . . I'm fine. It's just that . . . SOBS – 9 SEC.
CURTIS	I'm coming around.
JOANNA	. . . No . . .
CURTIS	I'll come right round.
JOANNA	SOBS – 3 SEC.

CALL 94 – TIMED 12.23 – THE SAME DAY

SIMON WEBB'S RECORDED ANSWER:
RECORDING OF *SPREAD A LITTLE HAPPINESS* STARTS.
Hello. Sorry there's no one here to answer your call at the moment, but if you'd like to leave a message for Simon Webb, or *ToyJoys, Ltd*, kindly do so after the bleep. Thank you.
BLEEP

SIMON WEBB:
Blast!

CALL 95 – TIMED 15.15 – THE SAME DAY

JOANNA WEBB:
(ANSWERING) Hello, (NUMBER WITHHELD).
DOROTHY GRISEWOOD:
Joanna, what a horror! Theft under our very noses! We're all scandalized, Joanna, scandalized. The Finnemores are distraught.

JOANNA . . . Very sweet of them.
DOROTHY Joanna, do borrow something.
JOANNA . . . We are managing.
DOROTHY There must be something you need.
JOANNA Tomorrow's organized like a military operation. We've made a running order of shops and Michael's fixed up a van. The new help's starting too.
DOROTHY That was quick. It takes me weeks to vet them. Double-check the references, Joanna. They can have very large pockets.
JOANNA For heaven's sake! There's nothing here for her to pocket.
DOROTHY How true! Joanna, you must want to borrow something . . . a futon? . . . a wok?
JOANNA . . . There's no need, Dorothy.
DOROTHY . . . A bean-bag?
JOANNA We really are coping.
DOROTHY Of course . . . Joanna . . . one thing.
JOANNA Yes?
DOROTHY Who were the little men selling burglar-alarms. They did seem rather effective.
JOANNA . . . *Thief Relief*.
DOROTHY *Thief Relief*. Splendid! Thank you so much.
JOANNA Not at all.
DOROTHY Better to be safe than sorry, isn't it?
JOANNA . . . Yes.

DOROTHY Goodbye, dear.
JOANNA . . . Yes.

CALL 96 – TIMED 19.23 – THE SAME DAY

JOANNA WEBB:
(ANSWERING) Hello, (NUMBER WITHHELD).
KIT WEBB:
Hi, mum.
JOANNA Kit!
KIT How's the simple life?
JOANNA Dreadfully complicated. Your father's seen the bank. There's already Rory's money and the bill for Ronald's car, but at least we're safe until we get the insurance.
KIT I thought a man in a three-piece came rushing around with a cheque. 'Don't fear the worst – We put clients first!'
JOANNA Our man's down with a cold.
KIT . . . Great!
JOANNA *Simon*! . . . Your father did say he wanted a word, dear. . . . *SIMON, IT'S KIT*! . . . He's become rather attached to the camp-bed. . . . *SIMON*!
BEDROOM PHONE CONNECTING
SIMON WEBB:
Kit?
KIT Hi, dad.
SIMON Kit, we'll have all the essentials in tomorrow, so you can move back.
KIT . . . Yeah? . . . Sure about that, dad? I could always . . .
SIMON I'm *sure*.
KIT . . . Dustin wouldn't . . .
SIMON You'll move back *tomorrow*, Kit.
BEDROOM PHONE DISCONNECTING
JOANNA WEBB:
That'll be lovely, dear.

KIT . . . Yeah.

JOANNA How's the *As U Like It*?

KIT Great! It's going to be a winner. They've got this really terrific designer, Howard Foss. Things are buzzy! We've been helping stick fake oak-leaves all over the *Forest of Arden Room*. Jerome . . . that's Mark Jerome, he's the owner . . . he said he'd never seen anything like the *Seven Ages of Man Bar*.

JOANNA . . . Lovely.

KIT It's the works! They've invited a lot of really glam people to the opening. Yeah . . . Bob Geldof, Mick and Jerry, Simon Callow, Lindsay Duncan . . . George Michael . . . Princess Michael . . . Jeremy Irons, Nick Revell . . . Sarah Brightman, Andrew Lloyd Webber and a mass of gossip columnists. Imagine! Real gossip columnists!

JOANNA . . . Yes. . . . Your father's moving around, dear. I'd better go.

KIT Okay, mum.

JOANNA We'll see you tomorrow.

KIT . . . Bye.

JOANNA Goodbye, dear.

CALL 97 – TIMED 19.52 – THE SAME DAY

VAL JESSOP:
Hello, Val . . . *Oogph*! . . . Jessop.

JOANNA WEBB:
(PHONING OUT) Val, it's only Joanna.

VAL *Eeugh*!

JOANNA Coping with Fern?

VAL Just about to eat, heart. She's invited Tanya round.

JOANNA *Val*!

VAL It's fine. Your daughter cooked the meal.

JOANNA *Cooked* the . . . ? Heavens! How's the kitchen?

VAL Retextured . . . Fern's right here.

FERN WEBB:

Mum? Val says I've got a great sense of colour.

JOANNA That's nice, dear.

FERN Yeah! She's got a liquidizer. I liquidized an onion, three red peppers, an avocado and some pilchards. It's a really great colour. Val says she's going to use the exact shade for the skin-tone of her *Post-Nuclear Social-Workers*. It's the best!

JOANNA . . . I see. . . . Fern, dear, I'll pick you up straight from school tomorrow. We should have all the basics by then.

FERN Sure. . . . Hold on, mum.

PAUSE IN CONVERSATION – 1 MIN 28 SEC.

Mum? Mrs Grisewood just called. She wants Tanya to go home.

JOANNA . . . She'd better go then, dear.

FERN She doesn't want to go.

JOANNA If her mother . . .

DOROTHY GRISEWOOD:

. . . MINUTE, THIS MINUTE, TANYA! . . . NOT WITHIN THESE FOUR WALLS!

JOANNA Fern, if . . .

DOROTHY:

. . . NEVER, NEVER! . . . JUST TRY THAT ONE AGAIN, JESSOP!

FERN . . . Mrs Grisewood's not very happy, mum.

JOANNA No . . .

FERN I'd better go. . . . Bye.

JOANNA *Fern*? . . . I'll come around. Fern, you mustn't . . .

DEAD LINE

CALL 98 – TIMED 20.36 – THE SAME DAY

SIMON WEBB:

(ANSWERING) Hello, Simon Webb.

	MICHAEL WEBB:
	Michael here, Simon.
SIMON	. . . Yes. . . . I've listened to your chat with Joanna.
MICHAEL	Uh huh?
SIMON	. . . Yes.
MICHAEL	Joanna's worried.
SIMON	So I gather.
MICHAEL	Genuinely worried, Simon. Why not just tell her what's happening? Some idiot making damn fool noises on the phone's not . . .
SIMON	Everything's all right, Michael.
MICHAEL	But . . .
SIMON	*Everything's all right.*
MICHAEL	It's not all right, dammit! Joanna's got enough on her plate without thinking . . .
SIMON	We've *all* got enough . . .
MICHAEL	You're . . .
SIMON	*EVERYTHING'S ALL BLOODY RIGHT!*
	PAUSE IN CONVERSATION – 4 SEC.
	DEAD LINE

CALL 99 – TIMED 23.04 – THE SAME DAY

	OPERATOR:
	Operator Services. Can I help you?
	SIMON WEBB:
	(PHONING OUT) Hello. *Achhht*! Could I have an alarm-call, please?
OPERATOR	Of course. What number?
SIMON	(NUMBER WITHHELD).
OPERATOR	. . . And when would you like it?
SIMON	Seven . . . No . . . *Achhht*! Hell! I think I'm better off on the floor. . . . No . . . six-thirty.
OPERATOR	. . . We'll call you at six-thirty.
SIMON	. . . *Achhht*!
OPERATOR	. . . Sleep well.

CALL 100 – TIMED 23.41 – THE SAME DAY

SWITCHBOARD MAN AT *RADIO THAMESIDE*:
Radio Thameside.

SIMON WEBB:
(PHONING OUT) Hello. It's the phone-in . . . *A Happy Home*. . . . I had a question.

MAN Name?

SIMON Uh . . . Steven.

MAN Where are you from, Steven?

SIMON . . . Bexleyheath.

MAN . . . Bexleyheath. . . . What's your question?

SIMON It's . . . It's rather personal.

MAN Oh, run a flag up! Someone wants to ask the sex-experts a personal question.

SIMON There's someone I know. . . . I'm worried he might be gay.

MAN . . . All right, Steven. Sit tight.

PAUSE IN CONVERSATION – 8 SEC.

BEN BARKER:
. . . so why not just keep smiling, Sharon?

CAROLINE DART:
Absolutely. Remember, you've always got *A Happy Home* waiting for you. And we've Steven from Bexleyheath on the line. Are you there, Steven?

SIMON . . . Hello?

CAROLINE Yes, Steven? . . . There's a question you'd like to ask?

SIMON Yes. It concerns . . . someone I know.

CAROLINE I see.

SIMON I think he might be gay.

CAROLINE Yes. . . . Yes, I see. . . . Ben?

BEN Right. We're used to people phoning up about their friends, Steven. How well do you know him?

SIMON Fairly well.

BEN I think you know him *very* well.

SIMON . . . Maybe . . .

BEN You're not helping yourself here, Steven.
SIMON . . . I'm sorry?
BEN It's *you* who's gay.
SIMON . . . No.
CAROLINE Relax, Steve. You've got *A Happy Home* here, and we can help you.
BEN How long have you known you were gay, Steve?
SIMON It's not *me*!
BEN It's never easy to open up. Look, Steve, there's nothing unusual about it. You've found you're attracted to someone of the same sex.
SIMON No way.
BEN . . . Take your time, Steve.
CAROLINE Absolutely.
BEN No one's rushing you.
CAROLINE Right.
BEN Take all the time in the world, Steve.
CAROLINE Who is it?

PAUSE IN CONVERSATION – 3 SEC.

SIMON It's my son.
BEN . . . Uh huh.
SIMON I . . . I don't know what to do about it.
BEN We understand.
CAROLINE Understanding's what it's all about, Steve.
SIMON . . . Yes.
BEN How long have you felt this way towards your son?
SIMON . . . *What*?
CAROLINE We do understand, Steve.
SIMON No, no . . . *no*!
CAROLINE Remember, you've got *A Happy Home* here. We can sort this out together.
BEN Sure we can. Steve, would you say this was a purely physical attraction?
SIMON Certainly not. There's no . . .
BEN It's emotional?
SIMON *No*.
CAROLINE You don't love your son, Steve?
SIMON *Of course I love my son*!

PAUSE IN CONVERSATION – 4 SEC.

CAROLINE I think we've got a breakthrough.

BEN Fine, Steve, you're doing just fine. Now take your time and tell us in your own words exactly what you feel for your son.

CAROLINE No one's rushing you, Steve.

BEN Right.

CAROLINE How far's this relationship gone?

SIMON *How* . . . ? Listen . . . my son's become involved with a friend of his.

BEN We get the picture.

CAROLINE Absolutely.

BEN You can't handle the jealousy.

SIMON . . . Why the hell should I be jealous?

CAROLINE Just how jealous are you, Steve?

BEN Take a scale of one to ten. Where are you?

SIMON I'm *not* jealous.

BEN That's about a six.

SIMON *I'm definitely not bloody jealous!*

BEN That's a ten!

CAROLINE Steve, I think you need help.

SIMON . . . I phoned in for . . .

BEN We're very glad you did phone in, Steve. I think we agree you ought to speak to someone about this.

CAROLINE Absolutely.

SIMON I am speaking . . .

BEN Steve, get help as soon as possible. You've one hell of a problem there.

CAROLINE And we've got another caller waiting.

BEN We'll put you back to the switchboard, Stevie. They'll give you some numbers.

CAROLINE And let us know how you get on, yes? Remember, you've always got *A Happy Home* waiting for you.

SIMON . . . Hello?

PAUSE IN CONVERSATION – 18 SEC.

SWITCHBOARD MAN:
Yes?

SIMON They said you'd give me some numbers.

MAN . . . What was your problem?

DEAD LINE

WEDNESDAY 19 MARCH

CALL 101 – TIMED 06.32

SIMON WEBB:
(ANSWERING) Whassat . . . ?
OPERATOR:
Is that (NUMBER WITHHELD)?

SIMON Whah . . . ?
OPERATOR . . . This is your six-thirty alarm call.
SIMON Whah . . . ? Whah . . . ?
OPERATOR . . . Hello?
SIMON . . . *Achhht*!
OPERATOR . . . Quite.

CALL 102 – TIMED 09.48 – THE SAME DAY

JOANNA WEBB:
(ANSWERING) Hello?
VAL JESSOP:
Joanna? It's Val.

JOANNA Val! . . . I do hope last night wasn't too embarrassing. I've never known Dorothy get quite so . . . well, quite so . . .
VAL Manic? Domineering? *Eeugh*! . . . Impossible?
JOANNA . . . Yes.

VAL Don't worry, heart. Nice of you to drop round.
JOANNA Nonsense.
VAL It's Tanya I feel sorry for. Imagine just sitting down to dinner and getting hauled away for fear of . . . uh . . . 'indoctrination by moral turpitude personified'.
JOANNA Oh, God!
VAL *Oogph*! She'll never see aubergines in quite the same way again.
JOANNA No . . .
VAL Fern went off to school like a shot. Longing to find out what a 'mutant Messalina' is, I expect. You'll be fully equipped to receive her back?
JOANNA Fingers crossed. Simon collected the van first thing. He's picking up the basics and I'm joining him as soon as I've got the new help started.
VAL *Urcht!*
JOANNA Val, I can't tell you how grateful I am. You'll have to come round as soon as we're functioning again.
VAL Love to.
JOANNA Val . . . what is a 'mutant Messalina'?
VAL Better ask Dorothy. . . . Bye, heart.
JOANNA . . . Bye, Val.

CALL 103 – TIMED 12.38 – THE SAME DAY

KEN (SURNAME UNKNOWN):
Yeah?
SHARON DUKES:
(PHONING OUT) Ken?
KEN Uh huh?
SHARON It's Sharon.
KEN Mmmm.
SHARON Busy?

KEN . . . Mmmm.
SHARON . . . I'm phoning from the Webbs.
KEN Uh huh.
SHARON There's not much cleaning to do. Everything's been nicked, Ken.
KEN Uh huh.
SHARON Mrs Webb said it all got burgled over the weekend.
KEN Uh huh.
SHARON Mr Webb's got a twitch.
KEN Mmmm.
SHARON They've gone shopping. There's a few things they need.
KEN Uh huh?
SHARON . . . How were the baps?
KEN Yeah.
SHARON Oh, good. . . . I think I'll go out for something.
KEN Mmmm.
SHARON Mrs Webb said I could make coffee on the *Primus*.
KEN Uh huh?
SHARON I think I'll go out for something.
KEN Uh huh.
SHARON Ken, there's a goose in the living-room.
KEN . . . Yeah?
SHARON Yes . . . a big, plaster goose. It glares at you.
KEN Mmmm.
SHARON Mr Webb said things should be back to normal soon. It's ever so odd. He looks right past you when he's speaking.
KEN Uh huh?
SHARON I don't know what to do, Ken. I've watered all the plants.
KEN Mmmm.
SHARON I could wash the goose.
KEN Uh huh?
SHARON There's nothing else . . . Oh, they're back. . . . Bye, Ken.
KEN . . . Mmmm.

CALL 104 – TIMED 13.22 – THE SAME DAY

SIMON WEBB:
(ANSWERING) Hello, Simon Webb.
KIT WEBB:
. . . Dad?

SIMON . . . Yes, Kit?
KIT . . . How's it going?
SIMON . . . Very . . . very . . . slowly.
KIT Dad, if you're still . . .
SIMON It's like moving in all over again. Traumatic! . . . Your mother keeps saying, 'It's quite a nice little house, really!' and finding walls we could knock down.
KIT . . . If things are that bad, wouldn't it be easier with me staying at . . . ?
SIMON God, this is costing!
KIT . . . Dad?
SIMON We've got another haul to make. Let's talk about it this evening.
KIT But Dustin . . .
SIMON *Kit*! We'll see you *tonight*!
KIT . . . Okay.
SIMON . . . Bye,then.
KIT . . . Yeah.

CALL 105 – TIMED 16.04 – THE SAME DAY

KEN (SURNAME UNKNOWN)**:**
Yeah?
SHARON DUKES:
(PHONING OUT) Ken?

KEN Uh huh.
SHARON Ken, it's ever so odd.
KEN Mmmm.
SHARON They keep coming in, dumping boxes, and going away again.

KEN Mmmm.

SHARON I'm all over packing. It's disheartening, Ken. The place was quite clean when I came to clean. . . . Mr Webb's done something to his back.

KEN Uh huh.

SHARON I did wash the goose.

KEN . . . Yeah?

SHARON A bit got chipped off its beak. It grins at you now.

KEN Uh huh.

SHARON . . . Were those baps as good as yesterday's?

KEN Mmmm.

SHARON You liked yesterday's.

KEN Mmmm.

SHARON What about tomorrow? D'you want them like yesterday's, or today's?

KEN Mmmm. *DO WE LOOK LIKE A RUDDY OFFICE-BLOCK? . . . TWO DOORS ALONG, YOU DAFT BUGGER!* . . . Yeah?

SHARON . . . Little problem?

KEN Uh huh.

SHARON What do you want . . . ? Oh, the van's back.

KEN Uh huh?

SHARON . . . Mrs Webb's helping Mr Webb out of the driving-seat. . . . Ooooo! There's more boxes!

KEN . . . Yeah?

SHARON . . . Bye, Ken.

KEN . . . Mmmm.

CALL 106 – TIMED 18.22 – THE SAME DAY

SIMON WEBB:
(ANSWERING) Hello, Simon Webb.

DOROTHY GRISEWOOD:
Simon? Dorothy Grisewood.

SIMON . . . Yes, Dorothy.

DOROTHY I wanted a quiet word.
SIMON . . . Yes?
DOROTHY Mrs Jessop!
SIMON . . . Yes?
DOROTHY Mrs Jessop, who was Mrs Clifton, who was Mrs McCulloch, nee Griffin.
SIMON . . . I think I can place her.
DOROTHY Simon, you'll have to be firm. It's appalling! I'd already made my views quite clear to Joanna, and what happens? My own daughter! My own daughter's inveigled into the Jessop menage and exposed to heaven knows what emotional trauma. I've had nightmares!
SIMON You've . . . ?
DOROTHY You'll have to make one thing quite clear. I won't tolerate my own child coming under the influence of that pornographic presence.
SIMON Dorothy . . .
DOROTHY *Do* something, Simon! I've spoken to Frank and we both absolutely insist that you *do* something. Immediately!
SIMON . . . How's Sebastian?
PAUSE IN CONVERSATION – 4 SEC.
DOROTHY I'm sorry?
SIMON . . . Sebastian . . . How is he?
DOROTHY . . . Oh, my God!
SIMON A little unwell, is he? Off-colour? A cause for concern?
DOROTHY . . . Simon! . . . Does anyone else know?
SIMON . . . Not yet.
DOROTHY Oh, Simon, no. . . . No, please, no.
SIMON I understand you were pretty rude last night. Perhaps you'd like to apologize to Joanna?
DOROTHY . . . It's . . . I've . . . If she happened to be there.
SIMON She does.
PAUSE IN CONVERSATION – 34 SEC.
JOANNA WEBB:
Dorothy?

DOROTHY . . . Yes.
JOANNA How are you?
DOROTHY . . . I'm . . . sorry. I'm really sorry.
JOANNA Yes?
DOROTHY . . . Yes.
JOANNA Dorothy, I'm a little lost.
DOROTHY . . . I was rude.
JOANNA Yes?
DOROTHY . . . Last night at Val's.
JOANNA Oh, yes.
DOROTHY . . . And I'm sorry.
JOANNA . . . Dorothy, is anything the matter?
DOROTHY . . . No. . . . I'm just sorry.
JOANNA Well . . . not at all. . . . Dorothy, we really ought to discuss this trip to Birmingham . . .
DOROTHY *Birmingham*! . . . Oh . . .
DEAD LINE

CALL 107 – TIMED 19.12 – THE SAME DAY

DUSTIN CAROWAY:
Hello?
KIT WEBB:
(PHONING OUT) Hi, Dustin.
DUSTIN Baby! Get back here!
KIT . . . Yeah.
DUSTIN Kilburn's got pretty lonely.
KIT There's no way at the moment, Dustin. Mum's gone mad getting my room together and she's having a really cruel time. Dad's started talking to the goose.
DUSTIN It's not your problem, Kit. Get the hell out!
KIT . . . I'm working on it.
DUSTIN Work very, very hard on it. Hey, Jerome turned up after you'd left the *As U Like It*.
KIT The man himself.
DUSTIN Right. He'd brought his lady with him. Jessica.

KIT Jessica? What's she like?

DUSTIN Mid-thirties, designer dungarees and no make-up.

KIT Mid-thirties and no make-up? Jeez! She's kept herself together.

DUSTIN She's fallen apart.

KIT You're serious?

DUSTIN Jerome's serious. Jessica gets a royal tour of the place, yeah, taking notes the whole time. Then they collar Dominic. Jerome says the *Forest of Arden Room*'s a knock-out. Apparently, it's really, really *there* and embodies the true ethos of a caring community.

KIT . . . What?

DUSTIN He was reading Jessica's notes.

KIT Where is that woman?

DUSTIN Stick around. She's not anti modern-dress, but the mirror-ball's too redolent of 1920's materialism, the statue of the wrestlers by the check-out's pugilistic, and there's a problem with the *Seven Ages of Man Bar*.

KIT Yeah?

DUSTIN It's sexist.

KIT . . . Great!

DUSTIN You want the full list? The *Touchstone Cocktail*'s not ideologically . . .

KIT Jerome's buying all this?

DUSTIN All on board. He says we can't afford to alienate the sub-cultures and alternative living-styles.

KIT How about alienating the designer? Howard's pumped his guts into the place.

DUSTIN Yeah. Dominic went off to phone him. He was looking thinner somehow.

KIT Who needs Jessica?

DUSTIN Jerome. It's her money he's spending.

KIT What a come-up!

DUSTIN Right. . . . Dominic says can we be in for eight?

KIT Jeez!

DUSTIN And talk to your parents, yes?
KIT . . . Yeah.
DUSTIN . . . See you at eight?
KIT . . . See you at eight.

CALL 108 – TIMED 19.38 – THE SAME DAY

TANYA GRISEWOOD:
Yes?
FERN WEBB:
(PHONING OUT) Hi, Tanya. I'm back home and it's one big mess. Mum's still reading the instructions for the new cooker, dad says he's not fitting another plug on anything till he's eaten and .he telly's not even wired up yet.

TANYA . . . You've no *telly*?
FERN Yeah, it's really exciting!
TANYA Wow! . . . It's awful here. Mum's gone all quiet. She's like she went when dad sacked the last gardener. Every time I ask her what's up she just says, 'Silence is golden!'
FERN Yeah?
TANYA Yeah. Nothing ever happens here. I wish we'd had a burglary.
FERN It's the best! I've got a new calculator, a new sports-bag, a new *Walkman* . . .
TANYA That's . . . really nice, Fern.
FERN . . . Only seven days to the Miles Ton concert, Tanya.
TANYA . . . Yeah.
FERN . . . Bye.

CALL 109 – TIMED 20.23 – THE SAME DAY

KIT WEBB:
(ANSWERING) The Webb residence.
RORY WEBB:
Kit?

KIT Rory! Great! Yeah! . . . Where are you?
RORY Isabel's. Where else?
KIT . . . You're paying for this? . . . *You*? From Barcelona?
RORY Sure. The cash came through from dad. I was calling to say thanks.
KIT I'll tell him. They're all out for a meal. Hey, I've got a job.
RORY Great!
KIT Jeez, it's a hassle! We're opening a restaurant Saturday and they've just decided to redesign the place. We're talking Armageddon. Oh, yeah. . . . Rory . . . there's something you should know about your stereo and all the garbage in your room.
RORY Yeah?
KIT It's not in your room. We've had wipe-out. Everything's been stolen.
RORY Christmas!
KIT Yeah. Dad seems to have got the insurance organized. You'll have to lay claim to your share. What a downer, eh? Us burgled, you mugged.
RORY . . . I wasn't mugged.
KIT . . . Dad said . . .
RORY I thought it might encourage him to shell out.
KIT Right.
RORY Not a word.
KIT Sure. Dad's twitching double-time anyway. He's getting really weird, Rory. Tonight he went into some ramble about Dorothy Grisewood.

RORY Dorothy?

KIT Yeah. He must have heard something. Dot's had a pretty rapid turnover in part-time help lately.

RORY I never complained.

KIT . . . Nor me.

RORY Dot's a one-woman sex-education department. She ought to be council funded.

KIT . . . It's just dad. He seems to be getting psychic.

RORY . . . How's Wanda?

KIT Yeah. . . . Jeez, I want to talk to you, Rory. When are you getting back?

RORY You mean, when am I leaving Isabel?

KIT . . . Maybe, I'll write.

RORY . . . What's up?

KIT . . . I'll write, Rory.

RORY Sure. Listen, love to everyone and tell dad thanks.

KIT Will do.

RORY Yeah . . . and love to Dorothy.

KIT . . . Huh!

THURSDAY 20 MARCH

CALL 110 – TIMED 09.16

JOANNA WEBB:
(ANSWERING) Hello, (NUMBER WITHHELD).
ROBIN CUDLIP:
Would that be M-m-m-Mrs Webb?

JOANNA Speaking.
ROBIN Is M-m-m . . .?
JOANNA I'm afraid not. He's in Ipswich all day.
ROBIN . . . Could you give him a m-m-m-message?
JOANNA Of course.
ROBIN It's Robin Cudlip, *Wonderland M-m-m-Magic*.
JOANNA . . . Yes?
ROBIN I'd like him to g-g-g-g . . .
JOANNA Get in touch?
ROBIN . . . g-g-g-get lost!
JOANNA . . . Oh!
ROBIN B-b-b-bye.
JOANNA . . . Goodbye, Mr Cudlip.

CALL 111 – TIMED 10.42 – THE SAME DAY

SWITCHBOARD GIRL AT *COMPUTRON*:
Hello, *Computron International*. Could you hold the line, please?

JOANNA WEBB:

(PHONING OUT) Yes.

PAUSE IN CONVERSATION – 2 MIN 17 SEC.

GIRL *Computron International*. Can I help you?

JOANNA Curtis Pine, please.

GIRL . . . Who's speaking?

JOANNA Joanna Webb.

GIRL I thought it was. How are you Mrs Webb?

JOANNA . . . Very well . . . thank you.

GIRL I'll just see if Mr Pine's available. What a morning!

PAUSE IN CONVERSATION – 19 SEC.

Mr Pine won't be long. Thank you for holding.

JOANNA . . . Do you have to play that . . . ?

RECORDING OF *RAVEL'S BOLERO* STARTS – 5 SEC.

Oh, no!

RECORDING OF *RAVEL'S BOLERO* CONTINUES – 1 MIN 23 SEC.

. . . *pom pompy pommm . . . py pompy pompy pompy pom pompy pommm . . . py pompy pompy pompy pom pompy pommm . . . py pompy pompy pompy pom pompy pommm . . . POM POMPY POMMM . . . PY POMPY POMPY POMPY POM . . .*

CURTIS PINE:

Hello?

JOANNA *POMPY POMMM . . . PY POMPY POMPY POMPY POM . . .*

CURTIS Joanna?

JOANNA *POMPY* . . . Oh, Curtis!

CURTIS You sound pretty cheerful.

JOANNA No, no. It's just that tape.

CURTIS Yes, it does help.

JOANNA . . . Yes. . . . Curtis, thank you for looking after my coat. I was feeling rather low, I'm afraid. It was good of you to come around.

CURTIS Not at all. You've no idea what a help you've been to *me*, Joanna.

JOANNA Good.

CURTIS . . . I just hate all this secrecy.

JOANNA . . . It won't be for much longer.
CURTIS . . . Let's hope.
JOANNA . . . Yes.
CURTIS You'll be free after the yoga tomorrow?
JOANNA Yes. Simon's staying overnight in Swindon. Curtis, let's not even go to the damned yoga class. We could relax somewhere.
CURTIS Wonderful!
JOANNA . . . Yes.
CURTIS Shall I call for you?
JOANNA No . . . Oh, what the hell! Yes. Why not?
CURTIS . . . I'll see you at seven.
JOANNA Lovely.
CURTIS . . . Till tomorrow.
JOANNA . . . Yes.

CALL 112 – TIMED 11.21 – THE SAME DAY

JOANNA WEBB:
(ANSWERING) Hello, (NUMBER WITHHELD).
BOB PRENTICE:
Bob Prentice, 'ere, *Little Tinkers*.

JOANNA . . . Yes, Mr Prentice.
BOB Tell Webb 'e's blown it. The man's lethal! Berks and business don't mix, love. . . . *GET YOUR STICKY FINGERS OFF*! . . . If I'd wanted *Little Single-Parents*, I'd have asked for *Little Single-Parents*. . . . *GET OUT*! . . . Tell 'im I've made other arrangements. Finito, okay?
JOANNA Yes . . .
BOB I don't want the prat on the premises.
JOANNA I see.
BOB You 'is wife?
JOANNA . . . Yes.
BOB Well, tell 'im that, will you?
JOANNA . . . Goodbye, Mr Prentice.

CALL 113 – TIMED 12.09 – THE SAME DAY

SHARON DUKES:
(ANSWERING) Hello?
SIMON WEBB:
. . . Hello?

SHARON . . . Yes?
SIMON (NUMBER WITHHELD)?
SHARON . . . Yes.
SIMON Oh! . . . That's Sharon.
SHARON . . . Yes.
SIMON It's Simon Webb.
SHARON . . . Yes?
SIMON . . . Get Joanna.
SHARON . . . Yes.

PAUSE IN CONVERSATION – 28 SEC.
JOANNA WEBB:
Simon? . . . Uh . . . *The bathroom, Sharon. You could clean the bathroom*. . . . Simon?

SIMON For God's sake, tell that girl how to answer a phone!
JOANNA . . . She does get nervous.
SIMON Nervous? On the phone? She's never off it.
JOANNA I hadn't noticed.
SIMON She's been . . . . . . I'm sure she was on the phone when we got back last night.
JOANNA . . . It's hardly the end of the world.
SIMON . . . I'm getting a telephone lock.
JOANNA *Simon*!
SIMON . . . Any messages?
JOANNA . . . I've . . . uh . . . written them down.
SIMON Good. I called in at the garage. Ronald's damned car should be ready tomorrow, so I'll use it to go to Swindon, stay over, and get it to Ludlow on Saturday.
JOANNA Oh, bless you!
SIMON It's a bloody imposition! . . . And Joanna . . . this jaunt that Dorothy's organized for Fern.
JOANNA . . . Yes?

SIMON	We'll have to cancel. . . . Fern can't go.
JOANNA	. . . That's ridiculous!
SIMON	Joanna . . . you don't *know* Dorothy.
JOANNA	. . . And you do?
SIMON	. . . I know enough.
JOANNA	What, Simon? Just tell me what? We can't do this to Fern.
SIMON	. . . Tell Sharon to wise up on the phone, okay? . . . Bye.
	DEAD LINE

CALL 114 – TIMED 12.23 – THE SAME DAY

KEN (SURNAME UNKNOWN):
Yeah?
SHARON DUKES:
(PHONING OUT) Ken?

KEN	Uh huh.
SHARON	I'm all of a quandary, Ken.
KEN	Uh huh.
SHARON	Mrs Webb's asked me to clean the bathroom twice.
KEN	Mmmm.
SHARON	She's in there now. I don't know what to do, Ken. She's crying.
KEN	. . . Yeah?
SHARON	I cleaned it as well as I could, Ken. Twice. I got all the little bits out round the taps.
KEN	Mmmm.
SHARON	It's much cleaner than ours.
KEN	Uh huh.
SHARON	. . . She's still crying.
KEN	Mmmm.
SHARON	I'm not sure how to help. I could water the plants.
KEN	Mmmm.
SHARON	I was wondering, Ken. You know we said we'd have pork-chops tonight, because you

like pork-chops, and they wouldn't take much time before your snooker, so that'd be nice and easy, and it's both of us really, we both like pork-chops?

KEN Mmmm.

SHARON Will a cottage pie be all right?

KEN . . . Uh huh.

SHARON I'll have to go, Ken. The loo's flushed.

KEN Mmmm.

SHARON Bye.

KEN Mmmm.

CALL 115 – TIMED 16.36 – THE SAME DAY

SHARON DUKES:
(ANSWERING) Hello, this is . . . uh . . . this is (NUMBER WITHHELD). Yes. . . . Can I help you?

DOROTHY GRISEWOOD:
Who the hell's that?

SHARON Uh . . . Sharon. I'm not at all nervous. I'm not really. Mrs Webb said she knew I wasn't really. . . . Can I help you?

DOROTHY God! Is Joanna there?

SHARON . . . Yes.

DOROTHY Get her!

SHARON . . . Who would that be . . . speaking?

DOROTHY Just get her!

PAUSE IN CONVERSATION – 2 MIN 17 SEC.

JOANNA WEBB:
Hello?

DOROTHY Joanna, I'm distraught!

JOANNA Dorothy?

DOROTHY . . . Constable Pattison's breathalized me.

JOANNA Breathalized!

DOROTHY Yes. Can you believe it? He produced that wretched little bag and said, 'Just keeping an eagle eye on the weasels!' Imagine it!

JOANNA . . . Yes.
DOROTHY I'd had nothing. Nothing at all. A quickie at the Finnemores, and I'd dropped into *Oxfam*. Geraldine had sold that musical cocktail-stick holder with the twiddling ballerina. Joanna, we've had it for eight years. A triumph! . . . I was just pulling out of the pub car-park.
JOANNA . . . How was the breathalizer?
DOROTHY Joanna, you've no idea! Two o'clock in the afternoon and I have to stand there in the middle of the street. . . . Blowing! . . . Imagine it!
JOANNA . . . Yes.
DOROTHY I'd not seen Constable Pattison as the type who'd smirk while breathalizing. Scales have fallen! Joanna, as my most valued friend . . . I didn't want you to hear it from anyone else.
JOANNA . . . Dorothy, how *was* the breathalizer?
DOROTHY . . . Positive.
JOANNA . . . Oh!
DOROTHY That filthy station! I shall appeal, have no doubts there. I'll fight it, Joanna. Think of the extenuating circumstances: one's nerves after your burglary; the musical cocktail-stick holder; ask yourself, is working for charity worth it?
JOANNA . . . Dorothy, I am sorry.
DOROTHY Joanna, we must stand shoulder to shoulder in these times of police oppression.
JOANNA Of course.
DOROTHY Thank you. I'm having a sustainer with the Finnemores. . . . Bye.
JOANNA . . . Goodbye, Dorothy.

CALL 116 – TIMED 19.54 – THE SAME DAY

FERN WEBB:
(ANSWERING) Hello?
TANYA GRISEWOOD:
Fern! Fern! Did you catch it? Miles Ton was giving an interview.

FERN I'm only just back.
TANYA Yeah?
FERN I'm being a model, Tanya. Val says I form the 'integral focus' for *Post-Nuclear Impressions*.
TANYA Wow!
FERN Yeah, modelling's great! I have to sit there and do nothing and represent hopeless pubescence. It's a huge painting. There's politicians wringing out handkerchiefs, social-workers – they're looking really harassed – and there's a huge, hovering figure Val calls *Ignorance*. It looks a bit like your mum.
TANYA Really?
FERN . . . Ever so much.
TANYA . . . Mum's not back yet. Mrs Finnemore phoned to say she'd had a little mishap, but they'll make sure she gets home all right. Dad says he gives up.
FERN Yeah?
TANYA Yeah.
FERN How was Miles Ton?
TANYA Great! They asked him if he liked touring and he said no, and they asked him why he'd changed his image and he said he hadn't, and they asked him if it was true about the paternity suit and he said he didn't want to answer that. He's the best!
FERN Yeah.
TANYA Hold on, Fern. . . . *DAD*! . . . *MUM'S BACK*! . . . Yeah. . . . *SHE'S JUST FALLEN OUT OF THE FINNEMORES' CAR*. . . . Bye, Fern.

FERN . . . Six days.
TANYA Yeah, six days. . . . Bye.

CALL 117 – TIMED 20.12 – THE SAME DAY

FERN WEBB:
(ANSWERING) Hello?
SERGEANT RAWLE:
Good evening. Would Mr Webb be around?
FERN He's not back.
SERGEANT Fair enough. You might tell him Sergeant Rawle phoned. It's regarding the break-in last Sunday.
FERN Sure. Mum can't believe dad forgot to lock the door.
PAUSE IN CONVERSATION – 4 SEC.
SERGEANT Which door would that be?
FERN The front-door.
SERGEANT . . . Your father forgot to lock the front-door?
FERN Yeah. The latch hasn't worked for ages and mum says he missed out on the mortice.
SERGEANT . . . I see.
FERN He really kicked himself.
SERGEANT . . . There was a broken window at the back.
FERN That's how *we* got in. The burglars had locked up after them.
SERGEANT *Bloody* . . . ! . . . Tell your father I'll be in touch, would you?
FERN Sure.
SERGEANT Goodnight, Miss Webb.
FERN Yeah. . . . Bye.

CALL 118 – TIMED 20.43 – THE SAME DAY

FERN WEBB:
(ANSWERING) Hello?
DUSTIN CAROWAY:
That Fern?

FERN Dustin? Hi, Dustin. What's up with Kit? He's zonked right out.
DUSTIN Can he make it to the phone?
FERN I'll check. Hey, I told Tanya all about your Metro and your 501's. She wants to look at you.
DUSTIN . . . Who's Tanya?
FERN She's my friend. When can she look at you?
DUSTIN . . . Yeah . . . uh . . . I'm pretty wiped myself, Fern. Could you find Kit?

PAUSE IN CONVERSATION – 1 MIN 31 SEC.

KIT WEBB:
Dustin?

DUSTIN Hi, there. . . . How is it?
KIT . . . Who needed today?
DUSTIN . . . None of us.
KIT . . . D'you think we'll see Jessica again?
DUSTIN Who knows? . . . It'll take her a while to get cleaned up. Two litres of gloss paint!
KIT . . . Sure.
DUSTIN You couldn't blame Howard.
KIT . . . Right.
DUSTIN No one could work with Jessica. She stalks round like a praying mantis on heat.
KIT . . . Yeah.
DUSTIN . . . Right.
KIT Howard loved that statue of the wrestlers. He didn't want to sit up all night making morris dancing costumes.
DUSTIN . . . Right.
KIT You think he's happy with two wrestling morris dancers?
DUSTIN No way.
KIT . . . He's done his best.

DUSTIN	. . . Sure.
KIT	Look at the *Seven Ages of People Bar*.
DUSTIN	. . . Great!
KIT	. . . Yeah.
DUSTIN	. . . What do you make of the chef?
KIT	Chef? . . . All he's got to do is open plastic-bags and shove the goodies in microwaves.
DUSTIN	. . . Yeah.
KIT	. . . I mean.
DUSTIN	. . . Sure.
KIT	. . . He's big though.
DUSTIN	He's big all right.
KIT	. . . . Jessica shouldn't have gone into the kitchen.
DUSTIN	. . . She wasn't there long.
KIT	. . . Right.
DUSTIN	Why should Howard care about ideologically sound cooking when he's halfway up an extension ladder?
KIT	Sure.
DUSTIN	. . . Gloss-paint's hellish to get out of the hair.
KIT	. . . Yeah.
DUSTIN	I saw Dominic having a quiet word with Jerome.
KIT	. . . Yeah?
DUSTIN	. . . D'you think we'll see Jessica again?
KIT	. . . Who knows?
DUSTIN	. . . Right.
KIT	. . . See you at eight?
DUSTIN	. . . See you at eight.

CALL 119 – TIMED 22.04 – THE SAME DAY

KIT WEBB:
(ANSWERING) The Webb residence.
WANDA POOL:
Kit? It's Wanda.

KIT . . . Hi, Wanda.
WANDA . . . I've missed your calls.
KIT . . . Yeah?
WANDA Everything's gone flat since the bust. How are you?
KIT I'm pretty flat myself, Wanda.
WANDA . . . Big Gut and Swastika are going to jump.
KIT . . . Jump?
WANDA Yeah, France. They don't fancy the idea of going inside.
KIT Sure.
WANDA There's a retreat Jason knows near Grenoble. It's some group called, *Les Amis Universels.*
KIT Yeah? . . . They sound friendly enough.
WANDA . . . You know them?
KIT . . . Not exactly, Wanda.
WANDA . . . Yeah, it was a toss-up, but they reckon it's marginally better than going inside.
KIT Right.
WANDA Swastika's nearly got enough to have his swastika removed, and Big Gut says the French really know how to find a natural rhythm to life. He's started smoking *Gitanes.*
KIT Yeah?
WANDA Jason reckons he'll move in here.
KIT . . . Oh!
WANDA . . . How's the diner?
KIT Don't ask! . . . You want to come to the opening Saturday? We can all invite someone.
WANDA . . . I'd have to check, Kit. Jason likes to get pretty philosophical on Saturday nights.
KIT . . . Sure.
WANDA You're having problems?
KIT I'm just wiped. I survived a blitz at the *As U Like It* today, then I get home and mum and dad are into the Cold War.
WANDA Who's winning?
KIT Fern. She says if dad stops mum from letting her go to the Miles Ton concert, she'll regard her promise to really try and stop leaving

her clothes all over everywhere as a wholly unrealistic concept.

WANDA . . . Yeah?

KIT . . . Don't forget Saturday at the *As U Like It*. You can't miss the place. There's a big neon sign in Walker Street, saying, '*As U Like It – The Food of Sweet and Bitter Fancy.*'

WANDA . . . I'll let you know, Kit.

KIT Sure. . . . Bye, Wanda.

WANDA . . . Chaio, now.

CALL 120 – TIMED 22.17 – THE SAME DAY

GEORGE MEADOWS:
Redhill (NUMBER WITHHELD).
SIMON WEBB:
(PHONING OUT) George?

GEORGE Talk of the devil! . . . *WAYNE*! . . . *GUESS WHO IT IS.*

SIMON . . . Wayne's there?

GEORGE *WHAHAY*! . . . *SPOT ON*! . . . Wayne says he'll see you at the *STEWS* meeting.

SIMON . . . Say hello for me.

GEORGE Sure. Are we going to have some night, Si. Wayne's divorce is through.

SIMON Yes?

GEORGE You know what this lunatic did? The day they untied the knot he sent Lois a *Tarzanogram*. LAUGHS – 7 SEC. Wayne had written him a little verse to say. 'You may be . . .' . . . *HOW DID IT GO, WAYNE*?
PAUSE IN CONVERSATION – 6 SEC.
That's it! 'You might be off your chump, But I'm too big to thump!' LAUGHS – 9 SEC. Then the guy had to kiss her.

SIMON Wayne's crazy.

GEORGE Right. The *Tarzanogram*'s suing.

SIMON What?

GEORGE He didn't come out of it too well. . . . You see, Si? Think of what Wayne must have been through.

SIMON . . . George . . .

GEORGE . . . Shoot!

PAUSE IN CONVERSATION – 4 SEC.

SIMON I've had it, George. . . . Joanna's . . .

GEORGE . . . Shoot, Si!

SIMON . . . She's . . .

GEORGE . . . Right.

SIMON . . . It's all hell, George. . . . Joanna . . . this damned burglary . . . the house is still a shambles . . . Fern's going to a Miles Ton concert . . . any moment now I'm going to get caned by the police . . . Joanna . . . money's vanishing right, left and centre . . . and business? . . . I'm not doing any bloody business.

GEORGE Shite!

SIMON . . . What's left, George?

GEORGE Yeah.

SIMON . . . Yes.

GEORGE . . . Fern's going to a Miles Ton concert?

SIMON . . . Yes.

GEORGE Shite!

SIMON . . . George?

GEORGE That's one mother of a scene.

SIMON . . . It's just that I need to talk . . .

GEORGE Course you do, Si. Spot on! We'll see you at the *STEWS* meeting.

SIMON . . . George . . . ?

GEORGE LAUGHS – 11 SEC. Whahay! . . . Si? . . . Wayne's juggling with his spurs.

SIMON . . . George . . . ?

GEORGE Bye, Si.

DEAD LINE

FRIDAY 21 MARCH

CALL 121 – TIMED 12.03

KEN (SURNAME UNKNOWN):
Yeah?
SHARON DUKES:
(PHONING OUT) Ken?

KEN Uh huh.
SHARON . . . You know when you answer the phone, Ken?
KEN Mmmm.
SHARON You ought to say who you are. Mrs Webb says it's most important to have a helpful telephone manner.
KEN Mmmm.
SHARON You could say, 'Hello, Belvedere Mansions, Hall Desk.'
KEN Uh huh.
SHARON . . . It'd be ever so helpful.
KEN Mmmm.
SHARON Mrs Webb told me.
KEN Uh huh.
SHARON Things are very upsy-down, Ken. The police were here when I arrived.
KEN . . . Yeah?
SHARON It was ever so odd.
KEN Mmmm?
SHARON Mrs Webb looked white and Mr Webb kept saying it couldn't be helped. . . . I've watered the plants.

KEN Mmmm.
SHARON . . . What's 'misleading information', Ken?
KEN Mmmm?
SHARON 'Misleading information'.
KEN Yeah . . .
SHARON It cropped up.
KEN Uh huh.
SHARON . . . The sergeant said something about weasels.
KEN Uh huh.
SHARON I'm using the bedroom phone. Mr Webb's put a lock on the other one.
KEN Uh huh.
SHARON . . . Have a go at it, Ken.
KEN Mmmm?
SHARON I'll phone up and you say, 'Hello, Belvedere Mansions.'
KEN Mmmm.
SHARON . . . Mrs Webb's back. . . . Bye, Ken.
KEN Mmmm.

CALL 122 – TIMED 13.21 – THE SAME DAY

JOANNA WEBB:
(ANSWERING) Hello, (NUMBER WITHHELD).
SIMON WEBB:
Joanna?

JOANNA . . . Simon.
SIMON I've picked up Ronald's flaming car. Hooper wasn't there, but I had to leave a cheque. D'you know how much we've forked out this week?
JOANNA You'll be able to settle up with father, Simon. Stop worrying. We'll have the insurance money soon.
SIMON . . . Yes.
JOANNA I can't see the problem.
SIMON . . . No.

JOANNA Well, then.
SIMON . . . Our daughter's got a mouth.
JOANNA *Simon*!
SIMON . . . Why talk to the police?
JOANNA . . . She'd been quite truthful.
SIMON And I hadn't? I never said a word, Joanna, not a word. The police arrived on Monday and shot round the house in three minutes flat. 'Got in through the back,' they said, 'Broke a window.' And I said, 'Really?'
JOANNA . . . Yes.
SIMON 'Really?' that's all I said. How can saying 'Really?' be giving misleading information?
JOANNA . . . It'll be all right.
SIMON Says you!
PAUSE IN CONVERSATION – 6 SEC.
JOANNA I'll let mother know you'll be arriving.
SIMON . . . Fine. . . . It'll be sometime tomorrow afternoon. The top speed on the damned thing's forty. It's got the shakes.
JOANNA . . . I know it's a bore, Simon, but I am grateful.
SIMON . . . Yes.
JOANNA How did you know it was Fern who told the police?
SIMON . . . What?
JOANNA They never mentioned Fern. How did you know it was her?
SIMON It had to be Fern, didn't it? They agreed it was Fern.
JOANNA . . . Eventually.
SIMON . . . Yes . . . ?
JOANNA It could have been anyone.
SIMON Really?
JOANNA . . . *Really*.
SIMON Have a good evening.
JOANNA . . . I'm sorry?
SIMON Have a bloody *good evening*!
JOANNA . . . Simon . . .
DEAD LINE

CALL 123 – TIMED 14.16 – THE SAME DAY

RONALD AGNEW:
Yes?
JOANNA WEBB:
(PHONING OUT) Hello? . . . Father?

RONALD Hello?
JOANNA Father, it's Joanna.
RONALD . . . Yes?
JOANNA How are you?
RONALD . . . Ronald Agnew speaking.
JOANNA . . . Father?
RONALD The little light started blinking.
JOANNA . . . IT'S JOANNA HERE.
RONALD Hello?
JOANNA . . . I WAS HOPING TO SPEAK TO MOTHER.
RONALD Hello?
JOANNA FATHER, SHALL I PHONE BACK LATER? WOULD THAT BE EASIER? . . . FATHER, I'LL PHONE BACK.
RONALD . . . Ronald Agnew speaking.
JOANNA I'LL PHONE BACK.
RONALD . . . Hello?
JOANNA I'LL PHONE BACK.
RONALD . . . Kate's here.
JOANNA I'LL PHONE . . . . . . Oh, thank God!

KATE AGNEW:
Yes, it is a blessing.

JOANNA . . . Mother?
KATE Ronald's so thrilled with the little light.
JOANNA . . . Yes.
KATE *RONALD, SIT DOWN! . . . SIT DOWN! . . . SIT!* . . . How are you, Joanna?
JOANNA Uh . . . very well. Mother, I was calling about your car. Simon should be there with it tomorrow afternoon.
KATE That's lovely.
JOANNA . . . He'll have to come straight back though.
KATE That's splendid.
JOANNA . . . And there will be the account to settle, mother.

KATE Isn't there always?
JOANNA . . . Yes . . .
KATE I've spoken to the twins, Joanna. They're coming here for Easter.
JOANNA How are they?
KATE So helpful, dear, so helpful.
JOANNA . . . That's nice.
KATE If it weren't for your brothers, dear . . . well . . .
JOANNA . . . Well?
KATE And Laura, of course. So thoughtful.
JOANNA Mother, Simon is driving all the way . . .
KATE It's having them so near, Joanna. That makes the difference. We're so close.
JOANNA . . . Yes.
KATE . . . February was a long month, wasn't it?
JOANNA February?
KATE . . . Long and cold.
JOANNA It was cold.
KATE Ronald's not fond of the cold.
JOANNA . . . No.
KATE Well, goodbye, dear.
JOANNA . . . Mother, Simon will need . . .
KATE *RONALD! . . . IF YOU MUST . . .*
JOANNA Goodbye, mother.

CALL 124 – TIMED 15.14 – THE SAME DAY

SHARON DUKES:
(ANSWERING) Hello, this is . . . uh . . . (NUMBER WITHHELD).
NORMAN HOOPER:
Mr Webb there?
SHARON Unfortunately, Mr Webb's not . . . here . . . or available.
NORMAN That Mrs Webb?
SHARON No. . . . No, it's not Mrs Webb. . . . Mrs Webb's just popped out for a wardrobe.

NORMAN . . . Has she now? . . . Tell Simon to phone me before he leaves for Ludlow, would you? It's very important.

SHARON . . . Yes?

NORMAN It's the *All Star Garage*.

SHARON . . . It's . . . ?

NORMAN Very important. Bye, now.

DEAD LINE

CALL 125 – TIMED 15.23 – THE SAME DAY

KEN (SURNAME UNKNOWN):
Yeah?

SHARON DUKES:
(PHONING OUT) No, Ken. No.

KEN Mmmm?

SHARON Say, 'Hello, this is Belvedere Mansions, Hall Desk.'

KEN Uh huh.

SHARON Say it, Ken. It's ever so helpful.

KEN Uh huh?

SHARON Of course it is.

KEN Mmmm.

SHARON . . . Someone gave me a message, but they phoned off before I got it.

KEN Yeah?

SHARON Yes. . . . The roof's leaking, Ken.

KEN . . . Uh huh.

SHARON I was doing the kitchen, but a man's arrived to repair the window. I don't know what to do now, Ken.

KEN Mmmm.

SHARON I could move the plants under the leak.

KEN Mmmm. . . . *TWO DOORS DOWN! . . . BLIND GIT!*

SHARON Oh, busy, busy.

KEN Mmmm.

SHARON . . . 'Hello, this is Belvedere Mansions.' Try to remember, Ken.
KEN Uh huh.
SHARON I'll see you later.
KEN Mmmm.
SHARON Bye, Ken.
KEN Mmmm.

CALL 126 – TIMED 19.04 – THE SAME DAY

SIMON WEBB'S RECORDED ANSWER:
RECORDING OF *SPREAD A LITTLE HAPPINESS* STARTS.
Hello, Sorry there's no one here to answer your call at the moment, but if you'd like to leave a message for Simon Webb, or *ToyJoys, Ltd*, kindly do so after the bleep. Thank you.
BLEEP
KIT WEBB:
Hi, mum. I was hoping to catch you before yoga. . . . Uh . . . I'm likely to be late tonight . . . like, really, really late. . . . The *As U Like It*'s . . . uh . . . not exactly finished. . . . Bye.

CALL 127 – TIMED 20.16 – THE SAME DAY

SIMON WEBB'S RECORDED ANSWER:
RECORDING OF *SPREAD A LITTLE HAPPINESS* STARTS.
Hello. Sorry there's no one here to answer your call at the moment, but if you'd like to leave a message for Simon Webb, or *ToyJoys, Ltd*, kindly do so after the bleep. Thank you.

JOANNA WEBB:
Kit, it's mum here. I'm at my . . . uh . . .
. . . Fern's seeing Tanya this evening, so if you could be there to let her in, dear. Bless you. I'll try not to be . . . uh. . . . . . Bye.

CALL 128 – TIMED 22.17 – THE SAME DAY

DOMINIC PARDY:
As U Like It.
FERN WEBB:
(PHONING OUT) Hello, could I speak to Kit Webb? It's his sister.

DOMINIC . . .Kit's busy right now.
FERN Yes, could I speak to him, please?
DOMINIC Get off the line! What d'ya think this is, a goddamn social club?
FERN . . . No, it's a restaurant. Kit said it was going to be a terrific restaurant with really glam customers and great service.
DOMINIC Get off the line!
FERN . . . I wanted to talk to him about the party-booking.
DOMINIC *KIT!*

PAUSE IN CONVERSATION – 3 MIN 28 SEC.
KIT WEBB:
Hello?

FERN Kit? Where's mum? There's nobody here.
KIT . . . Mum's not back?
FERN No. There's a message on the *Ansafast*, but she sounds . . . I dunno . . . confused. Mr Grisewood brought me home.
KIT Yeah? How d'you get in?
FERN Mr Grisewood smashed the back window. I showed him which one to smash.
KIT Oh, no! . . . Is Grisewood still there?
FERN He's gone for a tetanus jab.
KIT . . . Jeez!

FERN I got him bandaged up, but he made a terrible fuss, Kit. Why aren't you back?

KIT It's still chaos and the grand opening's tomorrow. I'm on special duty making sure Jessica doesn't get near Howard.

FERN Howard's the creep who answered the phone?

KIT No, that's Dominic. Howard's working flat out to get the place looking right; Dominic's working flat out to get Dominic looking right. We're all wiped!

FERN Yeah? . . . So what do I do, Kit?

KIT Do? Stay put, go to bed . . . whatever! Mum can't be too much longer.

FERN Why's she so late?

KIT . . . *JESSICA! . . . JEEZ! . . . NOT WHILE HE'S TAKING THE MIRROR-BALL DOWN!*

FERN . . . Kit . . . ?

KIT . . . *HOWARD* . . . ! . . . Bye, Fern.

CALL 129 – TIMED 23.56 – THE SAME DAY

KIT WEBB:

(ANSWERING) *Night Porter.*

PIPS

SIMON WEBB:

Kit?

KIT Hi, dad. . . . What's up?

SIMON . . . This hall's freezing.

KIT . . . Where are you?

SIMON Swindon. Mrs Worthy's redecorated the room. . . . Still no heating.

KIT . . . Hell!

SIMON . . . God, that wallpaper!

KIT . . . Yeah?

PAUSE IN CONVERSATION – 4 SEC.

Dad?

SIMON . . . Yes?

KIT You phoned up to talk about the wallpaper?
SIMON Of course not!
KIT It's just that I'm pretty whacked.
SIMON . . . It's ice-blue.
KIT . . . Dad?
SIMON . . . Your mother.
KIT . . . Yes?
SIMON . . . Is she in?
KIT No, she's not back yet. I'm only just here myself. It's been one bitch of a day at the *As U Like It*, dad. How many years bad luck d'you get for smashing two thousand mirrors?
SIMON . . . It's midnight!
KIT Yeah . . . I'm pretty whacked.
SIMON . . . She's been home and gone out again?
KIT There wasn't anyone here when Grisewood brought Fern home. Oh, yeah, you know that small window?

PIPS

SIMON Blast! Kit, phone me back.
KIT Whatever . . . ?
SIMON It's Swindon (NUMBER WITHHELD).
KIT . . . Can't it . . . ?
SIMON No.
KIT . . . Okay.

DEAD LINE

SATURDAY 22 MARCH

CALL 130 – TIMED 00.23

SIMON WEBB:
Where the hell have you been?
KIT WEBB:
(PHONING OUT) Fern came down for a sandwich.

SIMON God!
KIT She said to say she hates to say it, but she hates you.
SIMON What now?
KIT It was a pretty general statement. . . . What's the problem, dad?
SIMON Nothing . . . nothing, really.
KIT No?
SIMON . . . Are you sure you know what you're doing?
KIT . . . Dad, it's half past twelve.
SIMON . . . I know, I know. . . . I'm freezing.
KIT And I'm wiped out, dammit!
SIMON . . . Kit . . . I know I've been . . . preoccupied lately. There hasn't been much time to talk.
KIT . . . You thought this might be a good moment?
SIMON . . . Dustin . . .
KIT . . . What about Dustin?
PAUSE IN CONVERSATION – 6 SEC.
SIMON Is Joanna back?

KIT	No. . . . Stop, worrying, dad. People get pretty unwound with their yoga. Maybe they all fell asleep and nobody noticed.
SIMON	KIT, IT'S NO TIME FOR DAMN FOOL . . . !
	HILDA WORTHY:
	Mr Webb?
SIMON	. . . *Hilda*! . . . *Sorry* . . . . . . Bye, Kit.
KIT	. . . Bye, dad.

CALL 131 – TIMED 09.22 – THE SAME DAY

	JOANNA WEBB:
	(ANSWERING) Hello, (NUMBER WITHHELD).
	DUSTIN CAROWAY:
	Mrs Webb, it's Dustin. Is Kit still there?
JOANNA	Yes, Dustin. Hello. He's still in bed.
DUSTIN	. . . Oh, no!
JOANNA	Is he late?
DUSTIN	. . . Could you tell him Dominic's beginning to crack, the smocks have arrived for when we're waiting on table, the electricians were drunk before breakfast and we've got to help Howard with the finishing off? . . . Yeah, he's late.
JOANNA	. . . I'll tell him.
DUSTIN	Bye, Mrs Webb.

CALL 132 – TIMED 10.08 – THE SAME DAY

	JOANNA WEBB:
	(ANSWERING) Hello, (NUMBER WITHHELD).
	CURTIS PINE:
	. . . Joanna?
JOANNA	. . . Curtis. . . . Hello.
CURTIS	. . . Everything's falling into place.

JOANNA	. . . Good.
CURTIS	You've no idea what last night meant. . . . Just being able to . . . relate. . . . You can't know what it means.
JOANNA	Perhaps I can.
CURTIS	. . . It will work, Joanna. You'll see. I know it'll work.
JOANNA	If you're sure, I'm sure.
CURTIS	. . . Thank you.
JOANNA	. . . Thank *you*.
CURTIS	. . . Joanna, I'm in the States for ten days. As soon as I get back . . . I'll find you.
JOANNA	. . . Take care.
CURTIS	. . . Till then.
JOANNA	. . . Till then.
	PAUSE IN CONVERSATION – 5 SEC.
CURTIS	Goodbye, Joanna.
JOANNA	. . . Till then.

CALL 133 – TIMED 10.21 – THE SAME DAY

FRANK GRISEWOOD:
Grisewood here.
FERN WEBB:
(PHONING OUT) Mr Grisewood? It's Fern.

FRANK	. . . Yes.
FERN	How was the tetanus jab?
FRANK	. . . I had one.
FERN	Great! Hope the golf goes well, Mr Grisewood.
FRANK	. . . Did you want Tanya?
FERN	Please.
	PAUSE IN CONVERSATION – 59 SEC.

TANYA GRISEWOOD:
Hi, Fern.

FERN	Four days to go, Tanya! It's only four days!
TANYA	Yeah. . . . What was dad doing last night? His arm looks like the Invisible Man's, and

when I ask what happened he says he doesn't want to think about it.

FERN I got locked out. Your dad's just no good at breaking windows.

TANYA Wow! I wish I got locked out sometimes.

FERN Yeah.

TANYA Yeah, four days! Mum's bought us a cat-suit each. She keeps trying hers on and asking how she looks.

FERN Yeah?

TANYA Yeah.

FERN How does she look?

TANYA Yukky! She says it's for aerobics, but she tried it on with a fur coat over. It's for the Miles Ton concert.

FERN . . . I thought your mum was older than that.

TANYA She's a lot older than that.

FERN Yeah. . . . Mine says she wants to have a quiet day. She got really exhausted by the yoga. Can I come round?

TANYA Sure. . . . *BYE, DAD. . . . HAVE A GOOD TOURNAMENT!* . . . Come soon, Fern.

FERN I'm there.

CALL 134 – TIMED 13.56 – THE SAME DAY

JOANNA WEBB:
(ANSWERING) Hello, (NUMBER WITHHELD).

KIT WEBB:
Mum, it's Kit.

JOANNA Darling, were you very late?

KIT Forget it! Dominic's going spare anyway. Has Wanda phoned?

JOANNA I don't think so.

KIT Hell! They're trying to check numbers for tonight. One or two dozen people can't make it.

JOANNA . . . Oh?

KIT Jerome turned up half an hour ago and threw a wobbly over the lighting not being ready. That was before he found out nothing was ready. Chef got him to see our point of view though.

JOANNA That's good.

KIT He's a strong-minded chef. I'm still sweeping up the plates. Mum, if Wanda phones could you let me know, yea or nay?

JOANNA Of course, dear.

KIT . . . Hold on! . . . *JEEZ! OH, JEEZ!*

JOANNA . . . Kit?

KIT . . . *IT CAN'T HAVE!*

JOANNA What's . . . ?

KIT Power's gone. We've got total black-out. . . . Mum, I'll have to go.

JOANNA . . . We'll see you, Kit.

KIT Not here you wouldn't. . . . Bye.

JOANNA . . . Goodbye, dear.

CALL 135 – TIMED 14.42 – THE SAME DAY

JOANNA WEBB:
(ANSWERING) Hello, (NUMBER WITHHELD).

PIPS

SIMON WEBB:
Joanna?

JOANNA . . . Hello.

SIMON I'm only just leaving Swindon. Tell Kate . . . *If you don't mind that's my pint!*

JOANNA . . . Simon?

SIMON . . . *Not a very nice thing to say, is it? Flaming cheek!* . . . Tell Kate, I'll get there when I can.

JOANNA That's fine, Simon. It doesn't matter what time you arrive.

SIMON *SIMMER DOWN, CHUM, SIMMER DOWN!* . . .

Right. . . . You've no idea what it's like driving that thing. . . . How was the yoga?

JOANNA Oh . . . deadly dull. I shan't bother next term. It always give me a headache.

SIMON . . . How inconvenient!

JOANNA . . . I'm sorry?

SIMON Where the hell were you? I phoned at midnight.

JOANNA . . . I . . . dropped in to see Val. It never struck me you might phone.

SIMON Clearly.

JOANNA . . . Simon . . .

SIMON *Oh, God, so it is! . . . Sorry, chum.*

JOANNA . . . Simon . . .

SIMON *One pint of best, please. . . . ALL RIGHT! ALL RIGHT! . . . Sort of mistake anyone could make! . . .* Joanna?

JOANNA . . . Yes?

SIMON Where the hell were you? . . . ***ISN'T ANYBODY*** . . . ?

PIPS

. . . ***PINT OF BITTER, PLEASE!*** . . . Grisewood had to break that ruddy window to let Fern in.

JOANNA . . . I thought Kit would be here.

SIMON Thought? When did you last give any thought to anything? . . . ***I'M DOING MY DAMNED*** . . .

JOANNA . . . Simon? . . . Simon?

DEAD LINE

CALL 136 – TIMED 15.52 – THE SAME DAY

SIMON WEBB'S RECORDED ANSWER:

RECORDING OF *SPREAD A LITTLE HAPPINESS* STARTS

Hello. Sorry there's no one here to answer your call at the moment, but if you'd like to leave a message for Simon Webb, or *ToyJoys, Ltd*, kindly do so after the bleep. Thank you.

BLEEP

NORMAN HOOPER:

It's Norman here, *All Star Garage*. Hope you got the message, Simon. I told Stan that pile shouldn't have been collected. The mountings were still loose. Get in touch before you go tackling the Alps, would you? . . . Cheers, now.

CALL 137 – TIMED 16.12 – THE SAME DAY

JOANNA WEBB:

(ANSWERING) Hello, (NUMBER WITHHELD).

KATE AGNEW:

Joanna?

JOANNA Thank heavens! Mother, I've just had a message. Is Simon there?

KATE . . . No, dear.

JOANNA . . . Oh!

KATE Joanna, I'm afraid I've some rather terrible news.

JOANNA No! Mother! . . . What's happened?

KATE . . . It's something of a shock.

JOANNA . . . Yes?

KATE I am sorry to break it to you like this.

JOANNA . . . What's . . . ?

KATE I'm not sure how . . .

JOANNA Mother! . . . What's happened to Simon?

KATE Simon? . . . Nothing, dear, nothing to my knowledge.

JOANNA . . . Thank God!

KATE . . . Yes.

JOANNA Oh, what a relief! I'm so sorry, mother. . . . How are you?

KATE Trying to bear up, dear.

JOANNA Good. . . . And how's father?

KATE . . . He's dead.

PAUSE IN CONVERSATION – 4 SEC.

JOANNA *Dead?*

KATE . . . Mmmm.

JOANNA Mother! . . . I didn't realise.

KATE No.

JOANNA . . . When?

KATE . . . We were just having lunch, dear. . . . The Harpers had taken Ronald to the Garden Centre. He'd made another batch of geese and it was always something of a moment for him. . . . 'Just taking the geese to market,' he'd say. Well, you don't finish a goose in two minutes, dear. It's all the fiddly bits around the beak. Ronald would have names for them all by that time.

JOANNA . . . I know.

KATE . . . I was out levelling the rockery when they got back. . . . The geese were still in the Harpers' car. Ronald never said a word. Then . . . I'd just brought out the Red Leicester . . . he said, 'They didn't even want Wilfred.' . . . and he went.

JOANNA . . . Oh!

KATE Simply passed over.

JOANNA . . . Yes.

KATE . . . Went.

JOANNA . . . Mother . . .

KATE The doctor's been, of course.

JOANNA . . . Mother, Simon should be with you soon.

KATE That's hardly necessary, dear.

JOANNA . . . But he's on his way!

KATE No, no. The twins are coming over with Laura. I'll be quite all right.

JOANNA Simon's driving Ronald's car back, mother.

KATE . . . Ronald's slipped away, dear.

JOANNA . . . *Mother* . . . Simon should be nearly there. God willing. I know it's not the moment, but . . . I wouldn't mention it, of course . . .

KATE . . . Yes, dear?

JOANNA . . . There was the bill for the car. Simon's paid it.

KATE Quite.

JOANNA It was eight hundred and forty pounds!

KATE . . . *Never!* . . . Oh, thank heavens!

JOANNA . . . Mother?

KATE What a mercy!

JOANNA . . . Mercy?

KATE If Ronald had lived to know that, it would have killed him.

JOANNA . . . Mother, Simon should be . . .

KATE *COMING!* . . . The twins are here, Joanna. Splendid! . . . Goodbye.

JOANNA Mother!

KATE Goodbye, dear.

JOANNA . . . I'll phone.

KATE Yes, dear. . . . Goodbye.

JOANNA . . . Goodbye.

CALL 138 – TIMED 16.36 – THE SAME DAY

DOMINIC PARDY:
As U Like It.
JOANNA WEBB:
(PHONING OUT) Hello. Could I speak to Kit Webb? It's rather important.

DOMINIC No chance!

JOANNA . . . I do know you're very busy . . .

DOMINIC Get off the line!

JOANNA . . . It's his mother . . .

DOMINIC So what's this, a sodding creche?

JOANNA . . . It's-a-matter-of-life-and-death-for-goodness-sake-I'm-at-my-wit's-end-my-father's-just-passed-away-there's-no-one-here-to-talk-to-my-husband's-careering-round-the-country-with-loose-mountings-

and-you-surely-must-you-surely-must-must-must-be-able-to-ask-Kit-to-phone me!

DOMINIC . . . I'll ask him to phone.

JOANNA . . . Thank you.

DOMINIC . . . God help us!

CALL 139 – TIMED 16.43 – THE SAME DAY

VAL JESSOP:
Hello . . . *Eeugh!* . . . Val Jessop.

JOANNA WEBB:
(PHONING OUT) Val, it's Joanna. I'm not sure whether I'm coming or going. Simon's taken a car that's faulty and he's driving to Ludlow.

VAL Goodness! . . . *Oogph!* You're afraid he might not make it?

JOANNA He's taking it back to mother, but she doesn't want to see him.

VAL . . . You're afraid he *will* make it?

JOANNA No, no. Val, how are you on cars?

VAL . . . *Urcht!*

JOANNA What's a loose mounting?

VAL . . . Cars and loose mountings?

JOANNA Yes.

VAL . . . There's a connection?

JOANNA . . . Oh, dear! . . . I can't get hold of Simon, I can't get hold of Kit . . . . . . and my father's died.

VAL . . . Joanna!

JOANNA . . . Oh!

VAL I'll come round. . . . Give me . . . COUGHS – 8 SEC. . . . five minutes.

JOANNA . . . Oh!

VAL I'll be . . . *Awwgh!* . . . right there.

JOANNA . . . Bless you, Val.

CALL 140 – TIMED 18.28 – THE SAME DAY

JOANNA WEBB:
(ANSWERING) Yes? Hello? Simon?
KIT WEBB:
Mum, it's Kit. Got your message. Has Wanda phoned?

JOANNA . . . No, dear.
KIT Hell!
JOANNA . . . Kit, you have a moment?
KIT Yeah. We're changing into these tacky smocks. They've got '*As U Like It*' on the front, '*Did U Like It*?' on the back, and the stitching's coming undone. Why d'you phone?
JOANNA . . . Your grandfather's died.
KIT Yeah?
JOANNA . . . I'm afraid so.
KIT Right.
JOANNA . . . Yes. . . . And I was wondering if you knew what a loose mounting was.
KIT Grandad died of a loose mounting?
JOANNA No, no.
KIT Mum, I can't be too long. Things are getting pretty buzzy. We lost all the lights for an hour and Howard had to finish decorating with a torch. He's painted little *Orlandos* and *Rosalinds* on the loo doors. Yeah. Jerome's getting drunk with his lady in the *Seven Ages of People Bar*, and Dominic's told Howard he's not looking pretty enough to stay for the opening.
JOANNA . . . Poor man.
KIT Yeah, he's just stormed off.
JOANNA . . . I do hope the evening goes well, Kit.
KIT Right.
JOANNA Good luck.
KIT Yeah. . . . Hey, sorry about Granddad.
JOANNA . . . Yes.
KIT Gotta rush! Jeez! It's all about to happen, mum.

JOANNA . . . Go carefully.
KIT . . . See you later.

CALL 141 – TIMED 19.08 – THE SAME DAY

JOANNA WEBB:
(ANSWERING) Hello?
PIPS
SIMON WEBB:
Joanna?
JOANNA Simon! I've been frantic! Where are you?
SIMON Cheltenham.
JOANNA Thank God!
SIMON . . . What? The blasted car's falling apart, Joanna. I'm barely crawling.
JOANNA The repairs weren't finished, Simon. Come home!
SIMON . . . *Home*?
JOANNA You don't have to go to Ludlow.
SIMON . . . You're bloody joking!
JOANNA . . . Father's died.
SIMON . . . Died?
UNKNOWN MAN:
Directory Enquiries?
JOANNA I'm afraid so.
UNKNOWN MAN:
It's a Canterbury number.
SIMON You've got a crossed line.
UNKNOWN MAN:
Sorry?
SIMON Phone off! I'm just coping with a bereavement. Phone off, dammit!
UNKNOWN MAN:
A bereavement? Well, personal grief is one thing, isn't it? I understand personal grief, none more so. I'm not entirely sure we should let it affect our professional

standards though, should we? It's a Canterbury number.

SIMON Clear the bloody line!

UNKNOWN MAN:

Language! Is this why I bought *Telecom* shares? Good afternoon!

SIMON . . . Joanna?

JOANNA Yes?

SIMON I'll dump the car and get a train back. That's it, Joanna! I've had it!

JOANNA Simon . . .

DEAD LINE

SUNDAY 23 MARCH

CALL 142 – TIMED 10.32 – THE SAME DAY

FERN WEBB:
(ANSWERING) Yeah?
WANDA POOL:
Hi. Is Kit there?

FERN He's still crashed. That Wanda?

WANDA Yeah.

FERN Hi, Wanda. Everyone's still crashed. Dad arrived back in the middle of the night, like really early this morning, and he woke everyone up and Kit said dad was a bastard and he wanted to sleep for a week. I'll go and get him.

WANDA No, don't . . .

FERN *KIT! . . . KIT!*

PAUSE IN CONVERSATION – 4 MIN 26 SEC.

KIT WEBB:
Wanda?

WANDA You okay?

KIT Dead. Things were so revved up last night, I haven't really slept.

WANDA Sorry we couldn't make it.

KIT . . . No sweat.

WANDA Jason had fixed up a 'Get to Know Nietzsche Night' in Walthamstow. I'm not feeling too hot myself.

KIT Sure.

WANDA How were the famous faces?

KIT	What famous faces?
WANDA	. . . Nobody showed?
KIT	A lot of nobodies showed. We got half a dozen free-loaders, two gossip writers and a punch-drunk photographer.
WANDA	Yeah?
KIT	I'm dead. Yeah. . . . Oh, Jeez!
WANDA	. . . What?
KIT	It's all coming back. . . . Jerome got pretty high and bounced some prat. He'd found him in the loo with his lady. Did I tell you about Jessica?
WANDA	No.
KIT	Forget Jessica. Point is, it wasn't the guy's fault. Howard had painted little *Orlandos* and *Rosalinds* on the loo doors. One problem. He'd painted Rosalind dressed as a boy.
WANDA	Who's . . . ?
KIT	Things got a bit complicated. Yeah, one actor showed up. Someone said he was from the *Royal Shakespeare Company*.
WANDA	. . . Yeah?
KIT	He took one look and asked if he could just use the phone. They got photographs of him ringing another restaurant.
WANDA	. . . Sounds wild.
KIT	Yeah. When they finally got the lighting to work, all the fake oak-leaves dropped off. They took a photograph of me sweeping up.
WANDA	. . . I'd be interested to see that, Kit.
KIT	Yeah? One of the gossip writers kept saying, 'Autumn's come early in Arden!' Over and over. Jessica even laughed.
WANDA	. . . Arden . . . ?
KIT	Dominic told Jessica to shut up, Jerome told Dominic to shut up, Jessica told Jerome to shut up and went off with the columnist. . . . Jeez! Hang on, I'm finding a ciggy.
WANDA	Kit?

PAUSE IN CONVERSATION – 47 SEC.

KIT Yeah. . . . Howard made a come-back. Dominic had barred him from the opening for not looking pretty enough. Huh! You should have seen the ones who did show up.

WANDA Howard's the designer?

KIT Right. He'd only come back to piss over Dominic.

WANDA What did he do?

KIT He tried to piss over Dominic. Howard was looking damned good, actually. God knows what he's on!

WANDA Crazy!

KIT Dustin woke Chef up and asked him to get them sorted. Hell! Last thing Saturday night, I ask you? Have you ever tried phoning for an ambulance last thing Saturday?

WANDA . . . Not Saturday, no.

KIT Forty minutes. It was touch and go for Chef.

WANDA The *chef* got done over?

KIT Not quite. Howard had got Dominic on the nose and seems like Chef can't stand the sight of blood.

WANDA . . . He's a vegetarian chef?

KIT He's a microwave chef. Fainted clean out and cracked his head on the wrestling morris dancers. They got a photograph.

WANDA Well . . . like I said, Kit, I'm sorry we couldn't be there.

KIT . . . Listen, I'm going to re-crash. I'll be in touch, yeah?

WANDA Sure.

KIT Oh, Jeez! I just remembered. . . . My grandfather died.

WANDA Oh!

KIT Yeah. . . . Bye, Wanda.

WANDA . . . Chaio, now.

CALL 143 – TIMED 12.16 – THE SAME DAY

VAL JESSOP:
Eeugh! Urcht! . . . Oogph!
FERN WEBB:
(PHONING OUT) Hi, Val. Mum says can I come round and sit for you this afternoon?

VAL That's . . . *Awwgh!*

FERN Great! I think she's planning to have a row with dad. Mum's pretty considerate sometimes. How's the painting?

VAL COUGHS – 7 SEC.

FERN See you later, Val.

VAL . . . *Oogph!*

FERN . . . Bye.

CALL 144 – TIMED 12.47 – THE SAME DAY

GEORGE MEADOWS:
Redhill (NUMBER WITHHELD).
SIMON WEBB:
(PHONING OUT) George?

GEORGE Whahay! Great timing, Si. You wanna know about a *surprise*? I'll tell you about a *surprise*.

SIMON . . . What would that be, George?

GEORGE Here it comes. . . . *The Friend Who Stuck By His Woman*. . . . It's *your* song, Si. Finished it last night.

SIMON . . . George . . . ?

GEORGE Hang in there!
PAUSE IN CONVERSATION – 43 SEC.
Are you ready for this?
GUITAR UNDER
'I've a friend who stuck by his woman,
But he stuck so hard that it hurt –
Simon's heart simply had to be faithful,
He was clean, while his wife . . .'

SIMON *George!*
GEORGE . . . Knocked out, eh?
SIMON George, things are . . . I wanted to ask a favour.
GEORGE . . . Shoot, Si!
SIMON . . . How do you fancy a house-guest?
GEORGE . . . *You*?
SIMON . . . I thought maybe after Easter.
GEORGE Si? You're *leaving* Joanna?
SIMON . . . Yes.

PAUSE IN CONVERSATION – 5 SEC.

GEORGE No.
SIMON . . . George?
GEORGE I can't let you do this, Si.
SIMON . . . Why?
GEORGE Joanna's a nice lady.
SIMON . . . *What*?
GEORGE Can't you compromise, Si? You wanna know about *compromise*? I'll tell you about . . .
SIMON Don't give me this crap, George.
GEORGE . . . It's no crap.
SIMON Right from the start, you said . . .
GEORGE Think, Si, think! You wanna know about *divorce*? I'll tell you, we'll all tell you . . . it's a mug's game.
SIMON But the *STEWS*!
GEORGE . . . You want to end up like us?

PAUSE IN CONVERSATION – 3 SEC.

Exactly.
SIMON . . . George . . . I'm definitely leaving Joanna.

PAUSE IN CONVERSATION – 6 SEC.

GEORGE Si? . . . What about my *song*?

DEAD LINE

CALL 145 – TIMED 12.58 – THE SAME DAY

MICHAEL WEBB'S RECORDED ANSWER:
Hello, this is Michael Webb. Sorry I can't speak in person at the moment, but if you'd like to leave a . . .
SIMON WEBB:
(PHONING OUT) *Dammit!*
DEAD LINE

CALL 146 – TIMED 14.21 – THE SAME DAY

KATE AGNEW:
Hello? Ludlow (NUMBER WITHHELD).
JOANNA WEBB:
(PHONING OUT) Mother? It's Joanna.

KATE Yes, dear.
JOANNA . . . How are things?
KATE . . . We've kept busy.
JOANNA That's good.
KATE Quite. I'm not sure it's wise to be over-sentimental. If Ronald's gone, Ronald's gone.
JOANNA . . . Well . . .
KATE Rob thinks he can manage the horse-chestnut with a chain-saw.
JOANNA . . . The *horse-chestnut*?
KATE I shan't want anything *growing*, dear. The funeral might be Wednesday.
JOANNA . . . Yes?
KATE I only hope we can get the notice into the *Telegraph* in time. It's a major worry. The vicar came around last night and said a prayer.
JOANNA . . . He's always been very helpful.
KATE It'll be *No Flowers*.
JOANNA Ah! . . . I thought we might bring some of the . . .

KATE I do think not. Donations to a favourite charity.

JOANNA . . . I see.

KATE Your brothers have been a blessing. Rob's bagging up clothes and Laura's helping Martin clear out the junk in Ronald's study. Such energy! It's a pity Rob's never found a help-mate.

JOANNA . . . Yes.

KATE I suppose he'll find someone.

JOANNA I expect so.

KATE . . . *Oxfam*, maybe.

JOANNA . . . I'm sorry, mother?

KATE Your favourite charity.

JOANNA Oh, yes. . . . Probably.

KATE . . . It's a burial, of course. Ronald's had a double plot booked for years, but it's cremation for me, dear, do remember. There's no way I'm being boxed up and embedded in compost. . . . I've seen too much of it.

JOANNA TOO FAINT TO BE AUDIBLE – 6 SEC.

KATE Rob's starting the incinerator this afternoon.

JOANNA TOO FAINT TO BE AUDIBLE – 4 SEC.

KATE There's so much stuff, dear. Stuff! Ronald's stuff all over the place. And fire's so hygienic. . . . It's an ideal afternoon for the incinerator.

JOANNA TOO FAINT TO BE AUDIBLE – 4 SEC.

KATE Are you *saying* something, dear?

JOANNA . . . I said . . . 'It's quite nice here.'

KATE . . . Good.

JOANNA . . . Mother . . . uh . . . you said the funeral *might* be Wednesday?

KATE The vicar's having to check, dear. He's getting a little absent minded. We should know tomorrow.

JOANNA . . . I see.

KATE I've told your brothers, but do remember, dear, I won't be boxed up and embedded with Ronald.

JOANNA TOO FAINT TO BE AUDIBLE – 5 SEC.
KATE I'm sorry, dear?
JOANNA . . . Uh . . . I said, 'Goodbye, mother.'
KATE . . . Yes, goodbye.

CALL 147 – TIMED 14.59 – THE SAME DAY

KIT WEBB:
(ANSWERING) *Wuthering Heights.*
RORY WEBB:
Kit? . . . I'm coming home.
KIT Hey, Rory! That's terrific! . . . What's happened?
RORY Everything's turned sour, Kit. You wouldn't believe it. I got mugged.
KIT Yeah, you. . . . No, you didn't!
RORY Yes, I did. I got mugged, Thursday. Really mugged.
KIT Jeez! Did they get much?
RORY I didn't have anything on me. They weren't too crazy about that.
KIT . . . Right.
RORY My left eye's finally opened up again. . . . Hey, don't tell dad. He'd only worry.
KIT He was frantic about you being mugged when you weren't.
RORY Yes, but that was nothing to worry about.
KIT . . . Sure. . . . When are you getting back?
RORY Next weekend.
KIT Couldn't be better.
RORY . . . Dad there?
KIT . . . *DAD! . . . IT'S RORY!*
RORY . . . I've split with Isabel. That was really, like, ouch, Kit. She hated me having to scrounge.
KIT . . . Who'd she leave you for?
RORY No one. It's really embarrassing.
KIT Right.

RORY How's Wanda?
KIT . . . There's a lot I want to talk about, Rory. . . . Yeah. . . . Dad's here.
SIMON WEBB:
Rory?
RORY Dad, hi. I'm coming home.
SIMON Oh!
RORY *Oh*? What the hell's that? I thought we'd be into fatted-calf time.
SIMON . . . You told me you were mugged.
RORY . . . Right.
SIMON Were you, or were you not, mugged?
RORY . . . I was mugged.
SIMON Rory, I'm not a bloody fool! It never happened.
RORY . . . It happened all right. Listen, thanks for the loan. You can knock it off the insurance money you owe me.
SIMON *The* . . . !
RORY Let's talk about it, eh? I'll be back next Saturday.
SIMON . . . Too right, we'll talk.
RORY . . . How's mum?
SIMON . . . Yes. She's not too good. Your grandfather's died.
RORY Oh, no.
SIMON Apparently, Kate's destroying all the evidence.
RORY . . . *What*?
SIMON Evidence he ever existed.
RORY Oh! . . . Well, that's Kate.
SIMON . . . Saturday, then.
RORY . . . Sure. Put me back to Kit, would you?
SIMON Hang on.
PAUSE IN CONVERSATION – 17 SEC.
KIT WEBB:
Hi.
RORY Kit, you're a dickhead!
KIT . . . Rory?
RORY One, great, gabbing dickhead! . . . You split!
KIT . . . No way!

RORY	How else would dad have twigged I was pulling one?
KIT	. . . I dunno, Rory. I swear I . . .
RORY	Crap!
KIT	. . . Listen . . .
RORY	Keep out of my way, Kit!
KIT	. . . Rory . . . !
	DEAD LINE

CALL 148 – TIMED 15.31 – THE SAME DAY

	KIT WEBB:
	(ANSWERING) *Chamber of Horrors.*
	DUSTIN CAROWAY:
	Hi, baby. I'm just up.
KIT	Yeah? I wish I hadn't bothered.
DUSTIN	What's the problem?
KIT	. . . It's nothing. . . . Things have piled up. . . . Given last night, I can't see our jobs lasting. . . . My grandfather's died, gran's setting fire to everything, dad says he can't make the funeral and mum's rushed off to Val's in tears . . . and my brother's just called me a dickhead.
DUSTIN	Slow down, baby.
KIT	. . . It's nothing.
DUSTIN	. . . No?
KIT	Jeez!
DUSTIN	. . . Kit, get round here!
KIT	. . . I can't face anything, Dustin. . . . Sorry. . . . It's my birthday tomorrow.
DUSTIN	Baby! That's wonderful! You never. . . . What are we going to do?
KIT	. . . I just want to hide.
DUSTIN	. . . Kit? . . . I'm worried.
KIT	. . . It's nothing.
	PAUSE IN CONVERSATION – 7 SEC.
DUSTIN	I'll call tomorrow.

KIT . . . Sure.
DUSTIN You know where I am.
KIT . . . Yeah. . . . Thanks, Dustin.
DUSTIN . . . Bye, then.
KIT . . . Bye.

CALL 149 – TIMED 176.27 – THE SAME DAY

VAL JESSOP:
Urcht!
SIMON WEBB:
(PHONING OUT) Val? It's Simon.
VAL Splendid! . . . *Oogph!* . . . How's travelling, heart?
SIMON . . . It has its moments.
VAL *Awwgh!*
SIMON . . . Val, is Joanna still there?
VAL *JOANNA!* . . . I'm so grateful to Fern, Simon. *Post-Nuclear Pubescence* . . . *Eeugh!* . . . She's perfection.
SIMON . . . Yes?
VAL *Oogph!*
JOANNA WEBB:
Simon?
SIMON . . . I've just realised it's Kit's birthday tomorrow.
JOANNA . . . Yes?
SIMON Have we done anything about it?
JOANNA . . . Yes.
SIMON . . . Good.
PAUSE IN CONVERSATION – 4 SEC.
JOANNA Was that it?
SIMON . . . Yes.
JOANNA Well, that's most thoughtful of you, Simon. We'll. . . . Hold on. . . . Val says she's had an idea.
PAUSE IN CONVERSATION – 17 SEC.
Yes. . . . If you did have a moment, Val was

wondering if she could sketch you as the basis for . . . uh . . . the *Mourning Multilateralist*.

SIMON . . . I don't have a moment.

JOANNA No.

SIMON I'll see you later.

JOANNA . . . Of course.

SIMON . . . Goodbye, Joanna.

CALL 150 – TIMED 20.49 – THE SAME DAY

MICHAEL WEBB'S RECORDED ANSWER:

Hello, this is Michael Webb. Sorry I can't speak in person at the moment, but if you'd like to leave a message, please do so. Bleep coming up.

BLEEP

SIMON WEBB:

(PHONING OUT) It's Simon, here. Michael, if you're back tonight, phone me, would you? . . . Urgent. . . . Uh. . . . Bye, now.

MONDAY 24 MARCH

CALL 151 – TIMED 09.52

KIT WEBB:
(ANSWERING) The Webb residence.
DUSTIN CAROWAY:
'Happy birthday to you, Happy birthday to you, Happy birth . . .'

KIT Hi, Dustin.
DUSTIN You really should have said, baby. How are you feeling?
KIT . . . Hellish.
DUSTIN . . . What d'you get?
KIT You're kidding. Everyone had gone before I was up. Mum left me three cards.
DUSTIN Three?
KIT One from mum from dad, one from mum from Fern and one from mum from mum. I usually get one from Kate, but she was probably too busy incinerating Ronald's *Aertex*.
DUSTIN . . . How are we going to celebrate?
KIT Dustin, I'm sorry . . . I'm just not up to all this.
DUSTIN . . . Sure.
KIT . . . I've got to get my head together.
DUSTIN . . . Whatever you say.
KIT Sorry.
DUSTIN . . . Have you seen Dyson Flute's column?
KIT That jerk columnist?

DUSTIN The same. Must have been a thin news weekend. Guess what it's headed.

KIT . . . 'Autumn Comes Early in Arden'?

DUSTIN You've hit it.

KIT What a noodle!

DUSTIN Yeah. The whole page is berserk. He keeps going on about the 'glitterati'.

KIT Where do they come in?

DUSTIN All over. There's a photograph of Howard just before he landed one on Dominic, captioned, 'Manager Greets Top Designer'. Then there's, 'New Haunt for Top Theatre Company'.

KIT Yeah?

DUSTIN That's the *Royal Shakespeare* actor phoning another restaurant.

KIT . . . Who was he?

DUSTIN They can't have found out.

KIT Jeez!

DUSTIN 'Glitterati Party!' That's us when we got canned, waiting for the ambulance. And 'Top People Vote *As U Like It* Top Diner for Special Effects'.

KIT Falling oak-leaves?

DUSTIN Falling oak-leaves.

KIT . . . How?

DUSTIN Jessica must have swung it.

KIT Right.

DUSTIN . . . Let's meet.

KIT Dustin . . . . . . I'll call later.

DUSTIN . . . What is this?

KIT . . . I've got to think.

DUSTIN We've got a whole, gaping day free, Kit. No work till tomorrow. Surely . . . . . . Can't I help?

KIT . . . Not this time.

DUSTIN . . . I'll be here. Phone.

KIT Yeah.

DUSTIN . . . Bye, then.

KIT . . . Dustin . . . thanks.

DUSTIN . . . Happy birthday.

CALL 152 – TIMED 10.14 – THE SAME DAY

SIMON WEBB'S RECORDED ANSWER:
RECORDING OF *ALBINONI'S ADAGIO IN G* STARTS
Hello. Sorry there's no one here to answer your call at the moment, but if you'd like to leave a message for Simon Webb, or *ToyJoys, Ltd*, kindly do so after the bleep. Thank you.
BLEEP
RALPH BIFFEN:
Simon, it's Ralph Biffen, *ToyJoys. Heuff, heuff* . . . I'm Alan O'Connell's replacement. LAUGHS – 6 SEC . . . I've been checking . . . LAUGHS – 8 SEC . . . Give us a call, would you?

CALL 153 – TIMED 10.43 – THE SAME DAY

KIT WEBB:
(ANSWERING) The Webb residence.
JOANNA WEBB:
. . . Happy birthday, dear.

KIT . . . Thanks.
JOANNA . . . You've seen the paper?
KIT I just got one. I'm not sure I'm into talking about it, mum. . . . You're *Oxfamming*?
JOANNA Yes. . . . I don't know what time your father's back tonight, but I thought we might all pop out for a small celebration.
KIT . . . Don't worry about it.
JOANNA I realise . . . *Of course all the clothes have been cleaned*! . . . Kit, I know things have been rather scatty at home.
KIT . . . You've been okay, mum. You've worked bloody wonders. It's . . . Jeez! What is it with dad?

JOANNA . . . Yes.
KIT Well, *what*?
JOANNA . . . I'll be finished here soon. We can . . . *Eight pounds.*
KIT . . . Mum?
JOANNA *Yes, do try it on* . . . Kit?
KIT He didn't even remember, did he? My eighteenth and he didn't even bloody remember!
JOANNA Kit, we've all been . . .
KIT I know, I know. I don't give a lousy cuss about the birthday, but he's treating everyone like dirt. Everyone! How d'you stand it?
JOANNA . . . I tell myself . . . it wasn't like this before . . . and it can't go on for ever.
KIT Too right it can't. . . . Mum, I've got to get the hell out.
JOANNA . . . *That's lovely*!
KIT . . . *Mum*!
DEAD LINE

CALL 154 – TIMED 14.37 – THE SAME DAY

KATE AGNEW:
Hello? Ludlow (NUMBER WITHHELD).
JOANNA WEBB:
(PHONING OUT) Mother . . . how are you?
KATE Very busy, dear.
JOANNA . . . I was wondering about the arrangements.
KATE Really? Well, we've managed to clear Ronald's study, so Rob's moved in there on the put-you-up. We've still some way to go. So much won't burn, of course, and the bins are full up with geese. Martin's ordered a skip.

JOANNA ... I did mean arrangements for the funeral, mother.

KATE It's two-thirty, Wednesday.

JOANNA ... Two-thirty.

KATE The vicar dropped in again this morning and said another prayer. He's not what he was. Where would I have been without the twins?

JOANNA ... Yes.

KATE And Laura, of course. Such a comfort.

JOANNA ... We'll come to the house in good time.

KATE For whom, dear?

PAUSE IN CONVERSATION – 4 SEC.

JOANNA Goodbye, mother.

KATE Goodbye.

CALL 155 – TIMED 15.24 – THE SAME DAY

JOANNA WEBB:
(ANSWERING) Hello, (NUMBER WITHHELD).

SIMON WEBB:
... Joanna?

JOANNA Simon ... hello.

SIMON ... Yes?

JOANNA It's two-thirty, Wednesday.

SIMON ... All right. I suppose I could..

JOANNA ... Thank you.

SIMON I'll book us in somewhere. I've got to be in Luton the next morning.

JOANNA Good. It will give us more time.

SIMON ... For what?

JOANNA We have to talk, Simon.

SIMON ... I've seen Hooper. He's arranging for Ronald's car to be towed back.

JOANNA ... Fine. ... Simon, we must ...

SIMON Tell Kit ...

JOANNA ... Yes?

SIMON ... Nothing. ... I'll see you later.

JOANNA ... Simon ...
SIMON Bye, then.

CALL 156 – TIMED 15.53 – THE SAME DAY

JOANNA WEBB:
(ANSWERING) Hello, (NUMBER WITHHELD).
MONA GOODGE:
Mrs Webb?
JOANNA Speaking.
MONA It's Mona Goodge, here, Hillwater School. I'm afraid we've had something of a contretemps.
JOANNA ... Oh?
MONA I understand that Fern and Tanya Grisewood are in possession of tickets for a Miles Ton concert.
JOANNA ... Yes, that's right.
MONA I'm not sure that it was wise for them to mention it to their little friends.
JOANNA ... No?
MONA Possibly not quite so often. They both spent some time in the changing-room, Mrs Webb.
JOANNA ... They didn't have games today.
MONA Quite. It was some while before we noticed the barricade. Bearing all things in mind, perhaps someone could pick Fern up.
JOANNA Yes, of course. ... What things?
MONA They did miss lunch.
JOANNA *Lunch*? How long were they shut in?
MONA It was some while. We are trying to find the money to *heat* the changing-rooms.
JOANNA ... I'm on my way.
MONA Perhaps if they didn't mention the concert again, Mrs Webb.
JOANNA ... No.
MONA That might be wise. I've not managed to contact Mrs Grisewood yet.

JOANNA ... Oh, God!
MONA ... You know her?
JOANNA ... Yes. ... I'll look after Tanya.
MONA Thank you, Mrs Webb.
JOANNA ... Not at all.

CALL 157 – TIMED 20.04 – THE SAME DAY

DUSTIN CAROWAY:
Hello, (NUMBER WITHHELD).
KIT WEBB:
(PHONING OUT) Hi.
DUSTIN Kit! ... Great! ... What's the score?
KIT ... Can I hit Kilburn?
DUSTIN Terrific!
KIT ... I was thinking of bringing a suitcase.
DUSTIN ... Perfect.
KIT I'm with you.
DUSTIN ... Love you, baby.
KIT ... Yeah.

CALL 158 – TIMED 20.11 – THE SAME DAY

***RUNAROUND MINIS'* CONTROLLER:**
... *if it weren't raining*. Hold the line, please. ... *Car 15?* ... *Car 15?* ... *Runaround Minis.*
KIT WEBB:
(PHONING OUT) Yeah, could I have a car to 24, Tufnell Park Terrace?
CONTROLLER Sure.
DRIVER 15:
Car 15.
CONTROLLER *Car 15. Where are you?*

DRIVER 15:
Shepherds Bush and up yours, Jacko! Never mentioned the dogs, did you?

CONTROLLER *Never knew about the dogs.*

KIT Hello?

DRIVER 15:
Get that bloody animal under control!

CONTROLLER *Car 15. Pick up at the Kozee Kebab House, Queensway.*

DRIVER 15:
. . . Forget it!

KIT Hello?

CONTROLLER . . . What's the address?

KIT 24, Tufnell Park Terrace.

CONTROLLER . . . *Car 15*? . . . Any flat number?

KIT It's the house on the end. There's a hand-painted 'Burglar Beware!' sticker in the window.

CONTROLLER *Car 15*?

DRIVER 15:
Forget it!

CONTROLLER . . . *What's eating you?*

DRIVER 15:
Two bloody afghans! I'm off home. Forget it!

CONTROLLER *Car 15. . . . It's a non-British gent wants to see a good time.*

DRIVER 15:
Kozee Kebab House. On my way.

KIT Hello?

CONTROLLER 24, Tufnell Park Terrace?

KIT Yes.

CONTROLLER There in five minutes.

KIT Right.

CONTROLLER . . . *Car 9*?

CALL 159 – TIMED 20.23 – THE SAME DAY

KIT WEBB:
(ANSWERING) Yeah?

DOROTHY GRISEWOOD:
Kit? Get Joanna!

KIT . . . Dorothy?

DOROTHY Yes. Get Joanna!

KIT She's taken Fern out to dinner. It's my birthday treat.

DOROTHY . . . Are you aware of what Tanya's gone through?

KIT . . . Yeah.

DOROTHY I've quite simply never been so . . .

KIT Bye, Dorothy.

DEAD LINE

CALL 160 – TIMED 20.39 – THE SAME DAY

***RUNAROUND MINIS'* CONTROLLER:**
. . . without a bank-card. . . . Runaround Minis.

KIT WEBB:
(PHONING OUT) It's 24, Tufnell Park Terrace. Where's the damned car?

CONTROLLER . . . It's the rain. Sorry. . . . *Car 9? Car 9?* Slows everything down. . . . *Car 9?*

KIT I'm pretty desperate.

CONTROLLER . . . It's the rain. . . . *Car 9?*

DRIVER 15:
Car 15.

CONTROLLER *Yes, Car 15. Where are you?*

DRIVER 15:
Kozee Kebab House, Queensway. He's already found a good time. Up yours, Jacko!

CONTROLLER . . . *Car 9? Come in, Car 9.*

KIT Hello?

DRIVER 9:
Car 9.

CONTROLLER *Car 9. How far off Tufnell Park Terrace are you?*

DRIVER 9:
Where? . . . I told you I was . . .

DEAD LINE – 8 SEC.

CONTROLLER We'll be right with you. It's the rain.
KIT . . . Sure.

CALL 161 – TIMED 21.12 – THE SAME DAY

SIMON WEBB:
(ANSWERING) Hello, Simon Webb.
MICHAEL WEBB:
Simon? Sorry I couldn't get back to you last night. Problems.

SIMON . . . Ah!
MICHAEL . . . What's happened?
SIMON Michael . . . could you put me up for a while?
MICHAEL . . . Put you up?
SIMON I thought once we'd got Easter over.
MICHAEL . . . But why?
SIMON Thing's aren't too good. Joanna's . . . otherwised engaged.
PAUSE IN CONVERSATION – 4 SEC.
MICHAEL I don't believe it.
SIMON . . . I couldn't.
MICHAEL . . . Joanna?
SIMON Mmmm.
MICHAEL You've talked about this?
SIMON What's there to talk about? She doesn't know I know.
MICHAEL . . . It's impossible!
SIMON . . . I've got the tapes, Michael.
MICHAEL . . . Oh, my God!
PAUSE IN CONVERSATION – 7 SEC.
Of course you can stay, but . . .
SIMON Fine.
MICHAEL . . . Christ!
SIMON . . . What was the problem yesterday?
MICHAEL . . . I'm still not sure. I'd had a note. An *anonymous* note.
SIMON . . . Really?

MICHAEL It's unnerving. I'm beginning to understand how you felt about your obscene caller.

SIMON . . . What was the note?

MICHAEL Someone had chosen to inform me that Sally was . . . otherwise engaged . . . as you say.

PAUSE IN CONVERSATION – 5 SEC.

SIMON I see.

MICHAEL It freaked me. I stewed in a pub all night.

SIMON . . . Did they mention Sally by name?

MICHAEL Uh. . . . I'm not sure they did.

SIMON Don't worry. . . . They've made a mistake. It's not Sally.

MICHAEL . . . Who else . . . ?

SIMON Joanna.

MICHAEL . . . What are you talking about?

SIMON It's Joanna.

MICHAEL . . . How could . . . ?

SIMON God! Michael, d'you think I like knowing? Every bloody call that's been made on this phone, I know backwards. It's hell! Hell! . . . One of the ladies on your *Computron* switchboard thinks Joanna's your wife.

MICHAEL . . . My *wife*?

SIMON Yes. . . . She must have listened in, when Joanna was fixing up to meet . . .

MICHAEL . . . Curtis.

SIMON . . . Exactly.

MICHAEL . . . Thank heavens!

SIMON Michael, it's *hell*!

MICHAEL . . . Oh, yes. . . . Of course. . . . Sorry.

SIMON . . . There never was an obscene caller.

MICHAEL *What*?

SIMON They're back! . . . I'll phone, yes?

MICHAEL . . . Simon . . . ?

SIMON Bye, now.

CALL 162 – TIMED 21.33 – THE SAME DAY

TANYA GRISEWOOD:
Hello?
FERN WEBB:
(PHONING OUT) Hi, Tanya. Kit's left home and mum took me out to celebrate.

TANYA Yeah?

FERN It's Kit's birthday and he's acting really grown-up, Tanya. He said, 'Bugger this!', and walked out. He didn't even want to hear about us being locked in the changing-room all day.

TANYA No?

FERN Mum said she'd got the table booked and we might as well be miserable in a restaurant as miserable at home. It was great!

TANYA Wow!

FERN . . . Two days to go, Tanya.

TANYA . . . Yeah! Two days!

FERN Dad wasn't interested in us being shut in the changing-room either. He's just shut himself in the basement.

TANYA Yeah? My mum dragged dad back from a board-meeting to hear all about it. He's decided it's private for me from now on. Apparently, State Education's too expensive. Mum's not letting me go back.

FERN No? . . . What'll I do tomorrow?

TANYA I wouldn't mention the Miles Ton concert.

FERN . . . Right.

TANYA . . . Only two days! Wow!

FERN I'll let you know how school goes, Tanya.

TANYA Okay.

FERN Bye.

TANYA Bye, Fern.

CALL 163 – TIMED 21.46 – THE SAME DAY

SIMON WEBB:
(ANSWERING) Hello? Simon Webb.
***RUNAROUND MINIS'* CONTROLLER:**
24, Tufnell Park Terrace?

SIMON	Yes?
CONTROLLER	. . . Your minicab's outside.
SIMON	Scrub it! He left an hour ago.
CONTROLLER	Damn! . . . It's the rain.
SIMON	Bye.
CONTROLLER	Bye. . . . *Car 15*?

TUESDAY 25 MARCH

CALL 164 – TIMED 10.54

JOANNA WEBB:
(ANSWERING) Hello, (NUMBER WITHHELD).
DOROTHY GRISEWOOD:
Joanna? It's ignorance! Plain ignorance!

JOANNA Dorothy . . . ?

DOROTHY I tremble, Joanna. Education? How much education can two girls get locked in a changing-room all day? We pay rates! We pay taxes! For what, I ask you? For a staff of loony propagandists and failed drop-outs to encourage anarchy. . . . I'm writing to the Minister.

JOANNA . . . Yes?

DOROTHY . . . 'Why should we allow these precious, unformed minds to be shaped by such monsters? When a head-master . . .' . . . Hold on. I can't quite read . . . 'When a head-master thinks the incarceration of two blameless children in a changing-room a fit subject from which to draw parallels of a peculiarly Marxist nature, can he be morally qualified for the position entrusted to him? That man may say, "Children naturally loathe elitism," but I say, "Maxima debetur . . . puero . . . uh . . . reverentia."'

JOANNA . . . Yes?

DOROTHY . . . Often.

JOANNA . . . Dorothy, could you phone Kit for me?
DOROTHY Kit?
JOANNA Simon's locked both phones. I can't find the keys and I'm desperate to speak to Kit. He's on (NUMBER WITHHELD).
DOROTHY . . . Will *you* co-sign my letter to the minister?
JOANNA I'll sign any damned thing you like, Dorothy. Just get Kit to phone me. It's (NUMBER WITHHELD).
DOROTHY . . . Of course.
JOANNA . . . Oh, thank you. . . . Dorothy, *one* more thing . . . the concert.
DOROTHY Yes, I'll pick Fern straight up from school and we'll be right off to Birmingham.
JOANNA . . . It is . . . very noble of you.
DOROTHY Not at all. There must be worse things on earth than sitting through a Miles Ton concert. You do have your father's funeral.
JOANNA . . . Yes.
DOROTHY Must rush. I'm whisking Tanya off to find some white pancake and styling gel. I'm not entirely sure I understand punk chic.
JOANNA . . . Isn't Tanya a little . . . ?
DOROTHY It's hardly for her, dear. Bye.
JOANNA . . . Goodbye, Dorothy.

CALL 165 – TIMED 14.11 – THE SAME DAY

JOANNA WEBB:
(ANSWERING) Hello, (NUMBER WITHHELD).
VAL JESSOP:
COUGHS – 9 SEC.
JOANNA Hello, Val.
VAL *Oogph!* . . . Joanna? *Eeugh!* . . . I was wondering if Fern might manage the final sitting tonight.
JOANNA . . . I do think not tonight, Val. I've got to

get Fern fixed up for the concert tomorrow, and Simon ready for the funeral. I don't know which will be worse.

VAL Quite understand.

JOANNA Val . . . I'm completely stuck. The phones are both locked, Sharon appeared to clean up and just walked out five minutes later, I'm desperate to fetch Simon's dark suit from the cleaners, and I can't go out in case Kit phones.

VAL . . . *Urcht!*

JOANNA . . . Val?

VAL I'll be right there.

JOANNA Wonderful!

VAL . . . *Awwgh!*

JOANNA . . . Any chance of your calling in on Mrs Henry? She might have had second thoughts about working for us. If I've lost Sharon, I'll be frantic.

VAL Of course.

JOANNA . . . Bless you, Val.

VAL . . . *Oogph!*

CALL 166 – TIMED 15.38 – THE SAME DAY

JOANNA WEBB:
(ANSWERING) Hello, (NUMBER WITHHELD).

SHARON DUKES:
Hello? . . . Mrs Webb?

JOANNA Sharon! Hold on one moment. . . . *Val, I can't tell you how grateful I am. . . . I know it's still leaking. The Dimmocks have gone on holiday. . . . Bye, now. . . .* Hello, Sharon?

SHARON Yes, it's Sharon. I am sorry to slip off, Mrs Webb, but I had an emergency.

JOANNA . . . Ah!

SHARON Ken's baps! They were still in my bag and I couldn't even phone him.

JOANNA	No.
SHARON	Mrs Webb . . . it's not for me to say . . . but . . . well, it was Ken said it, really . . . it does seem odd that Mr Webb doesn't trust his own wife with the phone.
JOANNA	. . . Uh . . .
SHARON	See you Thursday.
JOANNA	. . . Sharon . . . actually, Mrs Henry was kind enough . . . DEAD LINE Damn!

CALL 167 – TIMED 15.43 – THE SAME DAY

SIMON WEBB'S RECORDED ANSWER:
RECORDING OF *ALBINONI'S ADAGIO IN G* STARTS
Hello. Sorry there's no one here to answer your call at the moment, but if you'd like to leave a message for Simon Webb, or *ToyJoys, Ltd*, kindly do so after the bleep. Thank you.
BLEEP
KIT WEBB:
Hi, mum. Dorothy said you wanted a call. I'll try again. . . . Bye.
JOANNA WEBB:
Kit? I'm here! I was just getting oil-paint off your father's clean suit. . . . Hello? . . . Kit? . . . Kit? . . . Blast!

CALL 168 – TIMED 18.54 – THE SAME DAY

FERN WEBB:
(ANSWERING) Hello?
RALPH BIFFEN:
. . . Could I speak to Simon Webb, please?

FERN	Yeah.
RALPH	. . . Tell him it's Ralph Biffen, the new Area Manager, *ToyJoys*.
FERN	*DAD! . . . SOMEONE ON THE PHONE!*
	PAUSE IN CONVERSATION – 1 MIN 12 SEC.
	SIMON WEBB:
	Hello?
RALPH	Simon? It's Ralph Biffen.
SIMON	Oh, Christ! . . . Sorry. Sorry, Ralph. Got your message. Uh . . . Lot of work on.
RALPH	*Heuff, heuff, heuff* . . .
SIMON	Ralph?
RALPH	LAUGHS – 5 SEC.
SIMON	. . . You mentioned Alan O'Connell had left.
RALPH	He has that. LAUGHS – 8 SEC.
SIMON	. . . Ah!
RALPH	His man of medicine recommended . . . *heuff, heuff* . . . an extended period of rest.
SIMON	. . . Poor chap.
RALPH	LAUGHS – 6 SEC.
SIMON	How's the computer?
RALPH	LAUGHS – 15 SEC.
SIMON	. . . Ralph?
RALPH	Drop into the office, would you, Simon?
SIMON	. . . Of course.
RALPH	. . . Tomorrow?
SIMON	Ah! I've got a funeral tomorrow.
RALPH	LAUGHS – 11 SEC.
SIMON	. . . I'll drop in Thursday afternoon.
RALPH	*Heuff, heuff, heuff* . . .
SIMON	Bye, Ralph.

CALL 169 – TIMED 19.12 – THE SAME DAY

FERN WEBB:

(PHONING OUT) . . . *always in the basement.*

HITLINE:

'. . . risk yah neck,
Till yah've grown as thin as yah Giro cheque,
Cos yah screwed yah mind when yah screwed that job,
So it's run, run, run like a no-hope slob,
But yah get knocked down by a blue Rolls Royce,
And the lady in the back, she yells, "Rejoice!" –
Cut the crap! Rejoice? Cut the crap!
Pump the cut the crap rap!
Then yah get kicked out by yah live-in chick,
Cos yah bawled too loud when she turned that trick,
But yah can't cut crap, with a half-assed curse,
And yah hope that hell can be no damn worse –
So yah down and limping on yah own two feet,
But they yell, "Who's you?", when yah hit that street –
Cut the crap! Who's you? Cut the crap!
Pump the cut the crap rap!
INSTRUMENTAL – 16 SEC.
Cut the crap! Who's you? Cut the crap!
Pump the cut the crap rap!
Sure, yah find some hole, but yah still don't fit,
Cos there ain't much hope and there's too much shit,
So yah suffer those off-beat, late-night gigs,
Where the all-star line-up's six-foot pigs,
Till yah . . .'
DEAD LINE

CALL 170 – TIMED 19.29 – THE SAME DAY

DOMINIC PARDY:
As U Like It.
JOANNA WEBB:
(PHONING OUT) . . . Oh! . . . Mr Pardy?
DOMINIC That's me.

JOANNA ... Look-I-really-am-dreadfully-sorry-to-disturb-you-again-and-I-certainly-wouldn't-if-it-wasn't-absolutely-essential-but-please-please-and-I-do-mean-absolutely-essential-I'm-desperate-frankly-please-could-you-possibly-find-time-to-pass-on-a-message-to Kit Webb.

DOMINIC ... Certainly.

JOANNA ... You will?

DOMINIC Of course.

JOANNA ... Would you ask him to phone home tonight? It doesn't matter how late.

DOMINIC Sure.

JOANNA ... That's really most kind.

DOMINIC It's always as you like it at the *As U Like It*.

JOANNA ... Uh ... yes.

DOMINIC ... Bye, now.

CALL 171 – TIMED 19.48 – THE SAME DAY

FERN WEBB:
(ANSWERING) Hello?

WANDA POOL:
Hi. Is Kit there?

FERN No. Hi, Wanda.

WANDA That Fern?

FERN Yeah. Kit's left home.

WANDA ... I don't believe it.

FERN I didn't want him to go, Wanda. I even promised I'd never mention Miles Ton to him again.

WANDA ... Miles Ton?

FERN Yeah. Tanya and I are going to his concert in Birmingham tomorrow. D'you like Miles Ton, Wanda?

WANDA He's ... uh ... yeah ... Miles Ton ... well ... yeah ... yeah ... he's really ... yeah ... Miles Ton ...

FERN Yeah, he's the best!
WANDA . . . Sure.
FERN . . . Kit was really down. It was his birthday yesterday and everyone forgot.
WANDA Ouch! I forgot.
FERN Everyone forgot except mum and she forgot to tell anyone. Things have been strange lately, Wanda. Kit'll be all right though. He's living with Dustin.
WANDA . . . Yeah?
FERN Dustin's terrific. He's got a Metro with stereo and Levi 501's.
WANDA I'm sure Kit's heading in the right direction. Jason says Nietzsche said you get a lot more out of life if you live dangerously.
FERN 501's are dangerous?
WANDA . . . It's . . . It's, like, the total concept, Fern.
FERN Yeah?
WANDA God, the *curry*! . . . Listen, if you see Kit, tell him I phoned.
FERN Sure.
WANDA Chaio, now.

CALL 172 – TIMED 20.31 – THE SAME DAY

OPERATOR:
Telecom Services. Can I help you?
SIMON WEBB:
(PHONING OUT) Yes, could I book an alarm-call, please?
OPERATOR Certainly. What's the number?
SIMON (NUMBER WITHHELD).
OPERATOR (NUMBER WITHHELD). And what time would you like it?
SIMON Six o'clock, please.
OPERATOR . . . We'll call you at six.
SIMON . . . *MILES TON'S A FLAMING GENIUS! YES!*

OPERATOR	. . . I'm not a fan, personally.
SIMON	Sorry?
OPERATOR	Goodnight, sir.

WEDNESDAY 26 MARCH

CALL 173 – TIMED 02.27

SIMON WEBB:
(ANSWERING) Whah . . . ? Whah . . . ?
KIT WEBB:
Dad?
SIMON Whassat . . . ?
JOANNA WEBB:
Hello?
KIT Hi, mum.
JOANNA Kit! . . . Lovely.
SIMON:
Whah . . . ? It's . . . half past . . . *Uchs!* . . . two.
JOANNA How are you, dear?
KIT Dead! What a night! The *As U Like It* was crammed to the fire-exits, mum. That rubbish in the paper really swung it for us.
JOANNA . . . *Try another half-tablet, dear.*
KIT . . . What?
JOANNA Your father. He'd only just got off and he's pacing again.
KIT Yeah?
JOANNA Kit, tomorrow . . . I mean, today. Is there any chance, and I do understand, but is there any chance . . . ? We're all away and it's just that another break-in. . . . We haven't even got the back window repaired again yet. Could you possibly be here, while we're away?

KIT . . . I've only just walked out.
JOANNA . . . I'd be worried sick.
KIT No one's going to be there at all?
JOANNA No.
KIT . . . Okay.
JOANNA Bless you, Kit. If you could just pop around during the day at some point and stay tomorrow night.
KIT . . . Sure.
JOANNA Would you like to speak to your father?
KIT No.
JOANNA . . . Kit, I am sorry things haven't . . .
KIT Not your problem, mum.
JOANNA . . . *At least sit down for a moment.*
KIT Dad still pounding the *Axminster*?
JOANNA . . . *It won't smell of turpentine tomorrow.*
KIT . . . Mum?
JOANNA . . . *Just another half-tablet.*
KIT Mum?
JOANNA Yes, dear?
KIT I'm crashing.
JOANNA Kit, thanks really.
KIT . . . Hope tomorrow's not too rough.
JOANNA Bless you.
KIT . . . Night then.
JOANNA Sleep well.

CALL 174 – TIMED 05.59 – THE SAME DAY

SIMON WEBB:
(ANSWERING) Whah . . . ?
OPERATOR:
Hello?
SIMON Whah . . . ? . . . Whah . . . ?
OPERATOR . . . This is your alarm . . .
SIMON Whassat . . . ? . . . must . . . must get cheque . . . *Uchs!* . . . bloody goose . . .
OPERATOR . . . Could you confirm . . . ?

SIMON	Whah . . . ? . . . wasn't misleading really . . . not really, really misleading . . .
OPERATOR	. . . This is your six am alarm call.
SIMON	. . . reeks of turps . . . *Uchs!* . . . friend who stuck by his woman . . . want to explain . . . *Uchs!* . . . want to explain . . .
OPERATOR	Hello? . . . *Hello*?
SIMON	. . . who needs *Cute Newts*?
	JOANNA WEBB:
	Hello?
OPERATOR	This is your six am alarm call.
JOANNA	. . . Thank you.
OPERATOR	. . . Best of luck.

CALL 175 – TIMED 09.52 – THE SAME DAY

SIMON WEBB'S RECORDED ANSWER:

RECORDING OF *ALBINONI'S ADAGIO IN G* STARTS.

Hello. Sorry there's no one here to answer your call at the moment, but if you'd like to leave a message for Simon Webb, or *ToyJoys, Ltd*, kindly do so after the bleep. Thank you.

BLEEP

MONA GOODGE:

Yes. . . . It's Miss Goodge here, Hillwater School. I'm making an exception to the personal message rule for the sake of goodwill. . . . Yes . . . Fern was hoping her brother might be there. She's forgotten her . . . uh . . . she's made a list . . . yes, she's forgotten her raincoat, her wash-bag, her *Walkman*, her Miles Ton cassettes . . . her *Miles Ton's on Top* T-Shirt, her *Miles Ton's on Top* badge . . . her money and her emergency money. I'd quite understand if you wanted to phone me back. . . . Goodbye, now.

CALL 176 – TIMED 12.36 – THE SAME DAY

SIMON WEBB'S RECORDED ANSWER:
RECORDING OF *ALBINONI'S ADAGIO IN G* STARTS.
Hello. Sorry there's no one here to answer your call at the moment, but if you'd like to leave a message for Simon Webb, or *ToyJoys, Ltd,* kindly do so after the bleep. Thank you.
BLEEP
LEONARD FRANKLIN:
Mr Webb? Leonard Franklin here of *Clover Cover Insurance*. . . . We have written to you, but I thought a personal word might be in order. I'm sorry to say we've now had some additional police information on your burglary and . . .
SIMON WEBB'S RECORDED ANSWER:
I'm afraid there's no room on the tape for a longer message at the moment. I'll get back to you as soon as possible. Thank you.

CALL 177 – TIMED 16.32 – THE SAME DAY

DUSTIN CAROWAY:
(ANSWERING) Hello?
SIMON WEBB:
. . . Hello? . . . Who's that?

DUSTIN Mr Webb?
SIMON . . . Yes?
DUSTIN . . . It's Dustin Caroway, Mr Webb.
SIMON . . . I see. . . . Is Kit there?
DUSTIN No, we forgot the putty.
SIMON . . . *Putty*?
DUSTIN I'm replacing your broken window, Mr Webb. I was going to get reinforced glass, but Kit said you might want to get in again sometime.

SIMON	. . . That's . . . good of you, Dustin.
DUSTIN	Anytime.
SIMON	. . . Dustin . . . ?
DUSTIN	Yes?
	PAUSE IN CONVERSATION – 6 SEC.
	Mr Webb?
SIMON	. . . Yes?
DUSTIN	. . . You sound pretty tired, Mr Webb. Can I give Kit a message?
SIMON	Ask him to phone Kate's, would you? His mother wants a word.
DUSTIN	Sure.
SIMON	. . . It's not been the most successful funeral.
DUSTIN	No?
SIMON	. . . We were rather hoping to have one.
DUSTIN	. . . Oh!
SIMON	. . . Dustin . . . ?
DUSTIN	. . . Yes?
SIMON	. . . Dustin, how do *your* parents feel?
DUSTIN	Oh, they're pretty fit. I think they'll be around for a while yet.
SIMON	No, no. I meant . . . how do they feel about *you*?
DUSTIN	. . . Me?
SIMON	Yes.
DUSTIN	Well, they are a bit over-indulgent. Look at me. Flat, car . . . allowance.
SIMON	. . . What does your father do?
DUSTIN	He's into Home Security.
SIMON	. . . I see.
DUSTIN	You could say he's a bit fast throwing his money around, I suppose.
SIMON	. . . What I'm trying to get at, Dustin . . . Kit's only . . . You must realise, I'm his father . . . There are . . . there are certain responsibilities . . . . . . It's an unknown world you're . . . . . . Ask Kit to phone his mother, would you?
DUSTIN	. . . Sure.
SIMON	. . . Dustin . . . I know you've got this job at

the moment, but would you mind my asking where your real ambitions lie?

DUSTIN That's a fair question, Mr Webb.

SIMON . . . Yes?

DUSTIN Essentially, I suppose I just want to hold on to the flat and the car. Dad's going broke.

SIMON . . . Ah!

DUSTIN I'll get Kit to phone then. If you'll excuse me, I'm still fixing your sash.

SIMON . . . Of course.

DUSTIN Have you ever thought of getting a burglar-alarm, Mr Webb?

SIMON . . . Goodbye, Dustin.

DUSTIN . . . Yes. Goodbye, Mr Webb.

CALL 178 – TIMED 16.51 – THE SAME DAY

KATE AGNEW:
Hello? Ludlow (NUMBER WITHHELD).

KIT WEBB:
(PHONING OUT) Hello, Kate? It's Kit.

KATE . . . Yes, dear.

KIT I was sorry to hear about granddad. How was the funeral?

KATE . . . It's just been one of those days.

KIT . . . Kate?

KATE Best laid plans, dear . . . many a slip . . . don't count them.

KIT . . . Sure.

KATE One moment, dear. . . . *MARTIN! ROB!* . . . The vicar's just arrived. There are one or two things to be said.

KIT Yeah? . . . Could I speak to mum, Kate?

KATE I think so. She was trying to keep your father awake somewhere. One moment.

PAUSE IN CONVERSATION – 43 SEC.

JOANNA WEBB:
Kit?

KIT Mum, what the hell's happening?

JOANNA Hush, dear. Rob and Martin are having a word with the vicar. I'm not sure the reverend's entirely well. He forgot the funeral.

KIT He *forgot*? How could anyone forget a funeral?

JOANNA I'm really not sure. He did forget a christening as well. We had to cut the service completely and the burial was rather rushed.

KIT Jeez!

JOANNA Hush, dear. . . . Oh! . . . Laura's at the piano. I think we're going to pray.

KIT Sounds reasonable.

JOANNA . . . Do hold on. I'll have to put the phone . . .

KIT . . . Mum?

PAUSE IN CONVERSATION – 14 SEC.

JOANNA '*. . . things bright and beautiful,*
All creatures great and small,
All things – mmmm, mmmm – *wonderful* –
Mmmm, mmmm – *God made them all.*

KIT Mum?

JOANNA '*Each little flower* – mmmm . . .' Yes, dear?

KIT There's been some messages.

JOANNA What messages? '*. . . ing colours . . .*'

KIT Fern's school phoned. She's forgotten a few items.

JOANNA '*. . . bright and beautiful . . .*' What items?

KIT . . . Everything.

JOANNA '*. . . great and small . . .*'

KIT And dad's insurance company left a message.

JOANNA '*. . . All things wise and wonderful . . .*'

KATE AGNEW:

JOANNA!

DEAD LINE

CALL 179 – TIMED 23.32 – THE SAME DAY

SIMON WEBB'S RECORDED ANSWER:
Hello. This is Simon Webb of *ToyJoys*. I'm afraid there's no room for any more messages on the tape at the moment. Perhaps you'd like to try again later. Thank you for . . .
DEAD LINE

CALL 180 – TIMED 23.54 – THE SAME DAY

SIMON WEBB'S RECORDED ANSWER:
Hello. This is Simon Webb of *ToyJoys*. I'm afraid . . .
DEAD LINE

THURSDAY 27 MARCH

CALL 181 – TIMED 00.54

SIMON WEBB'S RECORDED ANSWER:
Hello. This is Simon Webb . . .
DEAD LINE

CALL 182 – TIMED 01.47 – THE SAME DAY

KIT WEBB:
(ANSWERING) Yeah?
FERN WEBB:
Kit! . . . I've been ringing and ringing.

KIT Fern! . . . Jeez! . . . You know what the time is, Fern?

FERN It's a quarter to two.

KIT . . . Yeah. What's up? . . . You make out okay after losing all your things?

FERN Oh, sure. Mrs Grisewood bought me a load of stuff and got us fixed up with the hotel room and everything.

KIT So what's the hassle?

FERN We've lost Mrs Grisewood.

KIT . . . What?

FERN Mrs Grisewood's vanished.

KIT . . . Where the hell are you?

FERN Back at the hotel. . . . Everything was fine.

We checked in, got cleaned up, Mrs Grisewood changed into some pretty odd clothes . . . we had burgers with cheese, double fries, fritters and shakes. Yeah, it's weird! Tanya says her mum won't eat burgers in London.

KIT . . . Get to it, Fern.

FERN Mrs Grisewood looked real yukky. I suppose it was okay once the lasers started at the concert, but we got some extraordinary looks in the burger-bar. Tanya asked her to put her coat back on.

KIT . . . I get the picture.

FERN Yeah. She bought a *Miles Ton's on Top* badge to wear.

KIT Right. . . . So how was the concert?

FERN . . . We lost Mrs Grisewood.

KIT *Sure,* Fern. How?

FERN . . . Later it was pretty frightening. I mean, everyone scrambling, trying to get out of the hall at once. Mrs Grisewood gave us the room keys and said if we got separated to all meet back at the hotel. Yeah. Then she gave us some more money. . . . Then we got separated.

KIT Jeez! . . . That woman!

FERN Her room's next door. She's still not back.

KIT . . . Right.

FERN . . . The television's gone and closed down.

KIT Yeah. . . . *Thanks.*

FERN . . . What?

KIT Dustin's made coffee.

FERN . . . Dustin's there?

KIT . . . We're Neighbourhood Watching.

FERN Yeah? Tell him I'll tell him all about the concert.

KIT . . . How *was* the concert?

FERN We lost Mrs . . .

KIT For God's sake, how was *Miles Ton*?

FERN Oh! . . . He was all right.

KIT . . . Just all right?

FERN Kit, what do we *do*? Tanya wants to call the police.

KIT No, no. I'll . . . . . . I'm thinking, Fern.

PAUSE IN CONVERSATION – 7 SEC.

Listen, stay put. Dorothy must think you've tucked yourselves up and she's found a club or something.

FERN . . . A *club*?

KIT . . . Sure.

FERN This was supposed to be a treat, Kit. Tanya's been crying for two hours.

KIT Fern, I know Dorothy. She'll just breeze back in sometime soon. Relax. . . . What time . . . ? . . . Yeah. . . . Give her an hour or so.

FERN An *hour* . . . ?

KIT Sure. . . . Fern, grow up! Kid, I love you, but . . . just do this for me, yes?

PAUSE IN CONVERSATION – 4 SEC.

FERN Yes.

KIT That's my girl.

FERN . . . Kit?

KIT Yeah?

FERN Now you've left home . . . I sort of like you.

KIT . . . Okay. . . . Now bed, yes?

FERN Yes.

KIT Night, then.

FERN . . . *Shut it, Tanya*! . . . Goodnight, Kit. . . . Thanks.

CALL 183 – TIMED 03.29 – THE SAME DAY

KIT WEBB:

(ANSWERING) Awww . . .

FERN WEBB:

. . . Kit?

KIT . . . Uh huh?

FERN Mrs Grisewood's back.

KIT . . . Yeah?
FERN What do we do, Kit?
KIT . . . Do?
FERN Yeah. We'd just got to sleep. She's next door having a party.
KIT . . . *What*?
FERN She's next door having a party.
KIT . . . Jeez! . . . Hold on, Fern.
PAUSE IN CONVERSATION – 9 SEC.
Yeah. . . . Please.
FERN . . . Kit?
KIT . . . Dustin's making more coffee.
FERN . . . I wish I was there, Kit.
KIT Yeah? . . . What's happening?
FERN There was this one big racket . . . doors banging, guys shrieking . . . Tanya phoned down and complained.
KIT Yeah?
FERN Someone came up to get them quiet and we heard all this arguing. . . . It was Mrs Grisewood arguing.
KIT . . . Jeez!
FERN A lot of them stomped off. We went next door to say goodnight to Mrs Grisewood and . . . She's crazy, Kit! . . . She said wasn't it nice and she was having a little party with a personal friend.
KIT Oh, yeah? . . . Who?
FERN Miles Ton.
KIT . . . *What*?
FERN . . . She'd only just met Miles Ton and they're having a little party! . . . *Cut it, Tanya*! . . . What do I do?
KIT . . . Yeah.
FERN They're still giggling. . . . Miles Ton's a prat, Kit. He dribbles.
KIT . . . Really?
FERN We went next door and he just sat there and dribbled. Tanya started crying again. He's real yukky, Kit. . . . *Belt up, Tanya*! . . . His make-up's nearly as bad as Mrs Grisewood's. . . . What do I do?

KIT . . . There's not a lot . . .
CRASH
What in heaven. . . ? . . . Fern, what's happening?
CRASH . . . CRASH
PAUSE IN CRASHING – 4 SEC.
CRASH
FERN . . . Kit, what's happening?
CRASH
Kit!
KIT . . . Fern. . . ?
FERN Miles Ton's here. . . . Bye, Kit.
DEAD LINE

CALL 184 – TIMED 09.48 – THE SAME DAY

KIT WEBB:
(ANSWERING) Mmmm . . . ?
JOANNA WEBB:
Hello?
KIT . . . Yeah. . . ?
JOANNA Kit, it's mother. . . . How are you?
KIT . . . Asleep.
JOANNA I am sorry. . . . We were just leaving Ludlow. I thought I'd make sure everything was all right.
KIT . . . Sure.
JOANNA I don't suppose Dorothy's been in touch?
KIT . . . Not . . . yet.
JOANNA Fine.
KIT . . . *Strong and sweet*.
JOANNA Sorry, dear?
KIT . . . Dustin's making coffee.
JOANNA Oh, that's nice.
KIT Mum, just hold on, yeah? I'll try and kick-start some brain cells.
PAUSE IN CONVERSATION – 14 SEC.
What was it with the funeral?

JOANNA . . . Kit . . . don't ask.
KIT . . . It didn't sound as though . . .
JOANNA Mother's coming back with us.
KIT . . . *Kate*? *Why* for heaven's . . . ?
JOANNA Don't, Kit! . . . Please, *don't*!
KIT . . . Whatever you say.
JOANNA I just wanted to make sure Dorothy was coping.
KIT . . . Sure.
JOANNA Bless you, Kit. Your father's got some business calls, but we should be back this afternoon. . . . Thanks so much for being there.
KIT . . . Yeah.
JOANNA Go carefully.
KIT . . . Yeah.

CALL 185 – TIMED 10.23 – THE SAME DAY

KIT WEBB:
(ANSWERING) Yeah?
FERN WEBB:
Kit?
KIT . . . Hi, Fern.
FERN Mrs Grisewood's still snoring.
KIT . . . Would I was.
FERN We want to leave, Kit, but she's still flat out.
KIT . . . What happened to Miles Ton?
FERN He's on the floor.
KIT . . . That figures.
FERN Yeah. He's right here on the floor.
KIT *Your* floor?
FERN . . . Mrs Grisewood chased him in here. He managed to lock her out though. . . . He's still dribbling.
KIT Jeez! . . . *Miles Ton spent the night crashed on their floor*.
FERN . . . Dustin there?

KIT Yeah. . . . *Imagine*!
FERN About five-thirty, he threw up.
KIT . . . Great!
FERN Tanya used her *Miles Ton's on Top* T-Shirt to wipe him down.
KIT . . . Better let Dorothy just sleep it off. You've had breakfast?
FERN We didn't feel much like breakfast with Miles Ton . . .
KIT Sure.
FERN . . . *Tanya? Stuff it!*
KIT . . . Tanya still not coping too well? *Jeez!* . . . Hold on, Fern.
PAUSE IN CONVERSATION – 4 SEC.
Hi, Mrs Henry. . . . Mrs Henry, there's nothing to . . . . . . Oh, Jeez! . . . It's no sweat, Dustin . . . . Mrs Henry?
FERN . . . Hello?
KIT Fern, just stay put, dammit! Dorothy'll wake up soon and bring you home. Okay?
FERN Yeah, but . . .
KIT *Dustin! . . . She can't have fainted! . . . Mrs Henry . . .?*
DEAD LINE

CALL 186 – TIMED 10.40 – THE SAME DAY

KEN (SURNAME UNKNOWN):
Uh huh?
SHARON DUKES:
(PHONING OUT) Ken?
KEN Uh huh?
SHARON It's Sharon.
KEN Mmmm.
SHARON . . . I'm dropping around.
KEN Uh huh.
SHARON . . . It's ever so odd, Ken. I'd just arrived at the Webbs' and there was a lady walking out.

KEN . . . Yeah?
SHARON She said, 'Never again!'
KEN Uh huh.
SHARON 'Never again!' she said. 'Favours? Never again!'
KEN Mmmm.
SHARON . . . She was ever so pink. Ever so. She said she'd come to clean.
KEN Mmmm.
SHARON I said *I'd* come to clean.
KEN Uh huh?
SHARON . . . She said, 'Never again!'
KEN Mmm.
SHARON Then she said, 'Sodom and Gomorrah!'
KEN . . . Yeah?
SHARON . . . There's coffee cups everywhere.
KEN Mmmm.
SHARON The son's upstairs.
KEN Mmmm.
SHARON . . . He's nice. I like the son.
KEN Uh huh.
SHARON He said he'd do the clearing up, so I'm dropping around, Ken.
KEN Mmmm.
SHARON It's not that I'm not willing, but I'm not really needed.
KEN Mmmm.
SHARON . . . See you, then.
KEN Mmmm.

CALL 187 – TIMED 14.56 – THE SAME DAY

WANDA POOL:
Hi.
KIT WEBB:
(PHONING OUT) Wanda? It's Kit.
WANDA Kit! I've been trying to find you.
KIT Right.

WANDA . . . Sorry I missed your birthday.
KIT . . . Seems like a lifetime ago.
WANDA I've just been so, like, spaced out. It's since Jason moved in. . . . Newsflash – Big Gut's fixed up the retreat in France. He's off on Tuesday with Elastoplast Joe.
KIT . . . Yeah?
WANDA Stop Press – I'm going with them.
KIT . . . Really? . . . How come?
WANDA Jason says the retreat's a really good place to escape from the quintessential lie of modern technology.
KIT . . . You want to escape from modern technology, Wanda?
WANDA No, I want to escape from Jason.
KIT Right.
WANDA . . . We ought to meet up.
KIT Yeah. Fancy that evening at the *As U Like It*?
PAUSE IN CONVERSATION – 4 SEC.
We could go on somewhere.
WANDA . . . Sure.
KIT Saturday night? I'll book you in.
WANDA Fine. . . . Hey, how did Fern make out with the Miles Ton concert?
KIT . . . Yeah.
WANDA . . . It must have been wild for her.
KIT . . . You've hit the right area.
WANDA See you Saturday.
KIT . . . Sure. Bye, Wanda.
WANDA . . . Chaio, now.

CALL 188 – TIMED 18.08 – THE SAME DAY

FRANK GRISEWOOD:
Grisewood here.
SIMON WEBB:
(PHONING OUT) Frank? . . . Simon Webb.
FRANK . . . Yes?

SIMON . . . Family back yet?
FRANK . . . No.
SIMON Curious. . . . Frank, would you have half an hour?
FRANK Now?
SIMON Yes, now.
FRANK . . . Locked out again?
SIMON No.
FRANK . . . I really don't . . .
SIMON *Frank!*
FRANK . . . Yes?
SIMON Come . . . round . . . for . . . a . . . drink!

PAUSE IN CONVERSATION – 4 SEC.

FRANK Why?
SIMON *Just . . . come . . . round!*

PAUSE IN CONVERSATION – 6 SEC.

FRANK I'll come round.
SIMON . . . See you, Frank.

CALL 189 – TIMED 18.41 – THE SAME DAY

VAL JESSOP:
Hello, Val Jessop.
JOANNA WEBB:
(PHONING OUT) . . . Val?

VAL Joanna, you're home. . . . I've been thinking about you.
JOANNA . . . That's sweet.
VAL . . . Everything go smoothly?

PAUSE IN CONVERSATION – 5 SEC.

JOANNA Driving up . . . we passed father's old shooting-brake being towed back here. . . . That didn't help.
VAL . . . No.
JOANNA Poor old thing.
VAL . . . How was the service?
JOANNA . . . Quite intimate.
VAL . . . That's nice.

JOANNA . . . Yes. . . . Mother's come back with us.

VAL Really? I thought the twins were looking after everything.

JOANNA The twins were looking after the twins. They'd decided mother should sell up and move into a bed-sit with them in Stockport. Mother thought no.

VAL . . . Yes.

JOANNA She'd been so strong. Then the vicar came back to the house and congratulated her on the new grandson. . . . She's come down for a little rest.

VAL . . . Very wise.

JOANNA . . . Val . . . you sound . . . different somehow.

VAL . . . Different? . . . A little neurotic maybe. I've stopped smoking.

JOANNA Ah! . . . That's it.

VAL I'm determined this time.

JOANNA Well done.

VAL . . . How did Fern enjoy the conert?

JOANNA Heavens, yes! She's not even back yet. Kit left a note saying she'd forgotten all her things, but not to worry as it hadn't made any difference. That's one relief.

VAL . . . I expect she's had the time of her life.

JOANNA Yes. . . . Simon's dragged Frank down into his basement for some reason. . . . Oh! . . . One moment, Val.

PAUSE IN CONVERSATION – 9 SEC.

Goodnight, Frank. . . . Frank? . . . Simon? Why's Frank . . .?

SIMON WEBB:

TOO FAINT TO BE AUDIBLE – 6 SEC. . . . had it coming!

JOANNA . . . *Simon!*

VAL . . . Hello?

JOANNA Val . . . Val, we'll speak soon.

VAL . . . Of course.

JOANNA I must . . . uh . . . sort mother out.

VAL . . . Bye, heart.

JOANNA . . . Bye.

CALL 190 – TIMED 20.33 – THE SAME DAY

JOANNA WEBB:
(ANSWERING) Hello?
VAL JESSOP:
Joanna? . . . Dorothy Grisewood's here! She's asked if she can stay!

JOANNA Dorothy? . . . Stay? With *you*?
VAL . . . Yes.
JOANNA Whatever's happened? She arrived here about an hour ago, pushed Fern through the door and shot off. Fern seems to be in a state of shock.
VAL Dorothy's definitely in shock. Why come to me? . . . She's gone straight to bed with a pile of tranquillizers.
JOANNA . . . I see.
VAL And a bottle of vodka.
JOANNA . . . I still don't see.
VAL . . . Mmmm.
JOANNA You don't think she'd . . . ?
VAL Oh, no. She took half a dozen tonic-waters as well.
JOANNA . . . Ah!
VAL . . . Hasn't Fern said anything?
JOANNA Can't get a peep out of her. It's extraordinary! She just said she wished Kit was here.
VAL . . . Well . . .
JOANNA . . . Yes . . .
VAL . . . Mmmm . . .
JOANNA . . . Speak soon?
VAL . . . Mmmm . . .
JOANNA . . . Bye.
VAL . . . Bye, heart.

CALL 191 – TIMED 20.51 – THE SAME DAY

FERN WEBB:
(PHONING OUT) . . . *even want to think about the concert.*
HITLINE:
. . . and good luck with the marzipan filling. Coming up on the *Hitline* now, it's Miles Ton with *Too Much, Too Soon*. Make with it, Miles.
INSTRUMENTAL – 3 SEC.
DEAD LINE

FRIDAY 28 MARCH

CALL 192 – TIMED 11.09

MICHAEL WEBB:
Hello, (NUMBER WITHHELD).
JOANNA WEBB:
(PHONING OUT) Michael? It's Joanna.

MICHAEL . . . Joanna?
JOANNA . . . Yes.
MICHAEL Ah-yes-Joanna-just-having-a-Good-Friday-lie-in. . . . Yes-nice-to-hear-from-you. . . . Yes-sorry-to-hear-about-your-father-must-be-a . . . difficult time. . . . Yes.
JOANNA . . . Michael? Is anything the matter?
MICHAEL No-no-no-no.
JOANNA . . . I was just making sure you'd be with us on Sunday.
MICHAEL . . . Sunday?
JOANNA Easter lunch. Michael, for goodness sake! We'll be expecting you and Sally, as per.
MICHAEL . . . Ah!
JOANNA . . . You've not made other plans?
MICHAEL No-no-no-no. . . . Uh. . . . Does Simon know about this?
JOANNA He's still in bed, but I'm sure he'll take it for granted. You're always here for Easter Sunday.
MICHAEL . . . Yes.
JOANNA . . . Michael, what's wrong?

MICHAEL . . . Nothing. Nothing at all, Joanna. . . . We'll see you on Sunday.
JOANNA . . . Lovely.
MICHAEL . . . God!
JOANNA Sorry?
MICHAEL . . . Goodbye, Joanna.
JOANNA . . . Yes. . . . Bye, Michael.

CALL 193 – TIMED 11.36 – THE SAME DAY

TANYA GRISEWOOD:
Hello?
FERN WEBB:
(PHONING OUT) Tanya, why's your mum at Val's?

TANYA . . . Yeah. . . . It was really awful.
FERN Everything's been awful.
TANYA . . . Yeah.
FERN What was *really* awful?
TANYA When we got back last night, dad was waiting for us. He seemed to know everything that had happened.
FERN . . . How?
TANYA I dunno, Fern. . . . I'd never seen him cry before. Mum sent me upstairs and they had this terrible row.
FERN Yeah?
TANYA Dad's language got worse than Miles Ton's. Things must be bad, Fern. He's cancelling all mum's credit cards.
FERN Wow!
TANYA She said she'd fight it to the Lords and left.
FERN . . . I am sorry, Tanya.
TANYA That trip was some treat. . . . Dad says I'm going to have to be very, very strong. We might have a week in Eastbourne.
FERN . . . Yeah?
TANYA . . . Yeah.

FERN	It's a lousy Easter. I was going to get Kit's old room, but now gran's got it.
TANYA	. . . I'll have to go, Fern. Dad's trying to scramble eggs.
FERN	. . . Yeah?
TANYA	. . . Bye.
FERN	. . . Bye, Tanya.

CALL 194 – TIMED 11.58 – THE SAME DAY

DUSTIN CAROWAY:
Hello, (NUMBER WITHHELD).
JOANNA WEBB:
(PHONING OUT) Dustin, hello. It's Joanna Webb.

DUSTIN	Hi, Mrs Webb.
JOANNA	. . . Would Kit be there?
DUSTIN	He's at the launderette.
JOANNA	. . . Gracious!
DUSTIN	. . . Yeah?
JOANNA	Not to worry. I was wondering if you'd both come to lunch on Sunday?
DUSTIN	Sounds good. . . . I'll check with Kit.
JOANNA	Lovely. Simon'll be delighted. . . . We should have the whole family.
DUSTIN	. . . I'm flattered.
JOANNA	Nonsense. Hope to see you on Sunday.
DUSTIN	. . . Fine.
JOANNA	. . . Goodbye, Dustin.
DUSTIN	. . . Yeah. Bye, now.

CALL 195 – TIMED 12.14 – THE SAME DAY

JOANNA WEBB:
(ANSWERING) Hello . . .
PIPS

KIT WEBB:

Mum?

JOANNA Kit, dear.

KIT I'm having a crisis, mum. You'll have to talk me through.

JOANNA . . . What . . . ?

KIT It's my first launderette.

JOANNA . . . Kit, there's nothing difficult . . .

KIT My nerve's gone. There's six empty machines. . . . I can't even decide which one to use.

JOANNA Have you got the right change?

KIT . . . Yeah.

JOANNA . . . Powder?

KIT I got a cup from the machine. It doesn't look a lot of powder.

JOANNA You don't need a lot of powder.

KIT . . . It's a dump, mum. There's a bag-person stretched out . . . and a pregnant lady. She's laughing at me.

JOANNA . . . Kit . . .

KIT I've chosen a machine. Hold on.

PAUSE IN CONVERSATION – 14 SEC.

There's a sock in it.

JOANNA . . . Yes, dear.

KIT What do I do with the sock?

JOANNA Leave it where they can find it.

KIT . . . It's not a good sock, mum. I can't see them rushing back.

JOANNA Put it on the top, dear. . . . I've just spoken to Dustin.

KIT . . . Yeah?

JOANNA You're both invited to lunch on Sunday.

KIT . . . Dad knows about this?

JOANNA We've *always* had a family Easter. You and Dustin . . .

KIT Mum! . . . There's a lot I've got to talk to you about.

JOANNA . . . Lovely.

KIT . . . I'm not sure we should come.

JOANNA Kit, it's a last attempt! . . . You know what

your father's been like. He's not making any contact with anything. Rory's back tomorrow and I thought if we all got together . . .

PIPS

KIT Hold on.

PAUSE IN CONVERSATION – 6 SEC.

Hello?

JOANNA . . . Your father had to call in at *ToyJoys* when we got back last night. He hasn't spoken to me since.

KIT . . . Okay, okay. I'll think about Sunday. . . . Now what do I do?

JOANNA . . . Make sure the door's closed.

KIT It's closed.

JOANNA Put your money in the slide and start the machine.

KIT Right.

PAUSE IN CONVERSATION – 19 SEC.

The bag-person keeps cursing *Oxfam*, mum.

JOANNA . . . Really?

KIT Jeez! There's a light! There's a red light saying soap! What do I . . . ?

JOANNA Put the powder in, Kit.

KIT Yeah?

JOANNA Open the flap in the top and put half the powder in the front bit and half in the back bit.

KIT Right. . . . How about the bleach?

JOANNA No bleach.

KIT I've bought some bleach.

JOANNA Forget it.

KIT . . . The pregnant lady's laughing at me.

JOANNA Just put the powder in, Kit.

KIT . . . Right.

PAUSE IN CONVERSATION – 21 SEC.

I've put the powder in.

JOANNA You haven't used too much?

KIT There wasn't too much.

JOANNA It looks nice and foamy?

KIT . . . It looks good.

JOANNA Well . . . that's fine, dear.

KIT . . . Great! . . . Yeah . . . *dad* . . . I just don't know how you stick it, mum.

JOANNA . . . He'll come round.

KIT . . . That's one big maybe.

JOANNA . . . How's the machine?

KIT Fine. . . . The machine's doing fine.

JOANNA Good.

KIT . . . When do I put the washing in?

PIPS

JOANNA Kit! . . . You've . . . ?

KIT I've used my last. . . . Jeez! . . . Hold on.

DEAD LINE

CALL 196 – TIMED 13.13 – THE SAME DAY

SALLY WIMBUSH:
Hello?

SIMON WEBB:
(PHONING OUT) Sally?

SALLY Hello, Simon. . . . I hear we're getting a lodger.

SIMON . . . Yes . . . if that's all right.

SALLY . . . It's your life, Simon. You want to speak to Michael?

SIMON . . . Please.

PAUSE IN CONVERSATION – 58 SEC.

MICHAEL WEBB:
Simon?

SIMON . . . Yes.

MICHAEL . . . You're still set on this?

SIMON . . . Yes. Michael, I shan't overstay. It's just a bed until I get myself sorted out.

MICHAEL . . . Sure.

SIMON . . . My job's gone.

MICHAEL *What*?

SIMON Three months notice. . . . Grand Order of the Boot.

MICHAEL . . . *No*.
SIMON . . . One good thing . . . LAUGHS – 8 SEC. . . . I shan't have to tell Joanna.
MICHAEL . . . Simon. . . .
SIMON Yes?
MICHAEL . . . Joanna's inviting everyone to lunch on Sunday.
SIMON . . . Christ!
MICHAEL She's still not mentioned it?
SIMON . . . I'm only just up. Joanna woke me to say she was rescuing Kit from a launderette.
MICHAEL You must *talk* to her, Simon.
SIMON I will, I will. . . . I need time. . . . I just thought it was better to get out after Easter.
MICHAEL . . . How the hell do we get *through* Easter?
SIMON . . . You didn't have to accept.
MICHAEL Simon, we've done it for years.
SIMON . . . Years, yes. . . . It's been years . . . and years . . .
MICHAEL . . . Simon?
PAUSE IN CONVERSATION – 4 SEC.
Simon?
SIMON . . . See you Sunday.
MICHAEL . . . Some prospect!
SIMON . . . Bye.

CALL 197 – TIMED 15.46 – THE SAME DAY

KATE AGNEW:
(ANSWERING) Hello, Ludlow . . . Oh, no. Of course it isn't. (NUMBER WITHHELD).
VAL JESSOP:
Eeugh! Awwgh! . . . Urcht!
KATE . . . Hello?
VAL . . . *Oogph!*
KATE . . . Are you quite well?
VAL *Awwgh!*
KATE . . . Hello?

VAL	. . . You must be Joanna's . . . *Eeugh!* . . . mother.
KATE	. . . I am.
VAL	Is she . . . *Urcht!* . . . there?
KATE	My daughter's shopping! Shopping on Good Friday, I ask you! . . . It's not my usual Easter.
VAL	. . . *Awwgh!*
KATE	And you would be?
VAL	Val . . . *Awwgh!* . . . Jessop.
KATE	Yes, I think my daughter's mentioned you. Don't you paint?
VAL	Yes.
KATE	. . . Ronald painted.
VAL	Really?
KATE	. . . Geese, mainly.
VAL	. . . *Eeugh!*
KATE	Yes.
VAL	. . . *Oogph!* . . . It's just that Dorothy's still here. . . . *Awwgh! Oogph! Eeugh!* . . . *Urcht!* . . . She's threatening legal action against Frank and Simon for conspiracy to defame. . . . Kit and Rory for malicious slander . . . *Oogph!* . . . and she's seeking a court order to prevent Joanna seeing Tanya.
KATE	. . . Who is Dorothy?
VAL	. . . Just a friend of the family.
KATE	. . . I'll mention it.
VAL	*Urcht!*
KATE	. . . Goodbye.
VAL	. . . *Awwgh!*

CALL 198 – TIMED 18.21 – THE SAME DAY

GEORGE MEADOWS:
Redhill (NUMBER WITHHELD).
SIMON WEBB:
George?

GEORGE Si? Whahay! . . . We're seeing you at the STEWS tomorrow?

SIMON . . . Yes.

GEORGE How's things on the home front?

SIMON . . . Pass.

GEORGE . . . Joanna?

SIMON You'll be able to make me a full member.

GEORGE . . . Shite!

SIMON . . . Yes.

GEORGE You're a hundred per cent?

SIMON I'm moving in with my brother next week.

GEORGE . . . What can I say?

SIMON . . . Join the club?

GEORGE Join the . . . Whahay! . . . *Andy*? . . . *You know what Simon just said*?

SIMON . . . Say hello to Andy.

GEORGE *I'll tell you what he said*. . . . Listen, Si . . . I'm sorry. You wanna know about *sorry*?

SIMON . . . What time tomorrow?

GEORGE Blast off at eight. . . . *Simon's split with Joanna. I said what can I say and he said . . .*

SIMON I'll see you at eight.

GEORGE *Join the . . .*

DEAD LINE

SATURDAY 29 MARCH

CALL 199 – TIMED 12.32

JOANNA WEBB:
(ANSWERING) Hello, (NUMBER WITHHELD).
VAL JESSOP:
Eeugh! . . . Dorothy's flown.

JOANNA . . . Never!

VAL Gone before I'd got up, heart. . . . *Urcht!* . . . Message in lipstick on the bathroom mirror – 'Forget me, D.G.'

JOANNA Heavens! D'you think she'll be all right?

VAL . . . She has left a forwarding address.

JOANNA . . . Last night she hardly seemed capable.

VAL She phoned a Sebastian someone.

JOANNA Oh?

VAL *Awwgh!* . . . Never seen anyone pull together so quickly, heart. . . . *Urcht!* . . . I can't say I'm sorry to lose her. *Oogph!*

JOANNA . . . I did feel for you, Val. And just as you'd stopped smoking.

VAL *Urcht!* . . . *Awwgh!*

JOANNA . . . Val?

VAL . . . *Oogph!*

JOANNA . . . Fern's desperate to see how your painting's coming on. She's taking mother to the fair, but I thought we might pop around later.

VAL . . . *Eucht!*

JOANNA . . . I hope he's rich.

VAL	. . . Who?
JOANNA	Sebastian.
VAL	. . . Oh, yes.
JOANNA	. . . Goodbye, Val.
VAL	. . . *Oogph!*

CALL 200 – TIMED 14.11 – THE SAME DAY

SIMON WEBB:
(ANSWERING) Hello, Simon . . .
PIPS
RORY WEBB:
Dad?

SIMON	. . . Hello, Rory.
RORY	Hi. . . . Yeah. . . . I've just hit Gatwick.
SIMON	. . . Good.
RORY	Busy?
SIMON	Very busy.
RORY	. . . Right.
SIMON	We'll see you, then.
RORY	Yeah. . . . You don't fancy a drive to a nice airport?
SIMON	No.
RORY	. . . Right. . . . How are you, dad?
SIMON	. . . Fine.
RORY	. . . Good.
SIMON	Rory . . . Kit didn't tell me you weren't mugged.
RORY	. . . No?
SIMON	No.
RORY	. . . I have been mugged.
SIMON	. . . Goodbye, Rory.
	PAUSE IN CONVERSATION – 4 SEC.
RORY	See you.

CALL 201 – TIMED 17.35 – THE SAME DAY

SIMON WEBB:
(ANSWERING) Hello, Simon Webb.
FRANK GRISEWOOD:
Simon?

SIMON Hello, Frank.
FRANK . . . Are you busy?
SIMON No.
FRANK . . . What do I do, Simon?
SIMON . . . Do?
FRANK . . . I never suspected, not for a moment. . . . Dorothy! . . . Listening to those conversations on tape. . . . You can't imagine how I felt.
SIMON . . . Can't I?
FRANK SOBS – 6 SEC.
SIMON Frank?
FRANK SOBS – 11 SEC. . . . Coconuts.
SIMON . . . I'm sorry?
FRANK Sorry? . . . What damn good's being sorry?
SIMON . . . I meant, sorry, what did you mean by 'coconuts'?
FRANK Oh! . . . SOBS 9 SEC.
SIMON . . . Frank?
FRANK . . . Dorothy always wanted me to win a coconut. SOBS – 3 SEC. . . . One of the first times we went out together, it was Hampstead Heath . . . the fair. I won a coconut for her. SOBS – 5 SEC. . . . It became a rather special moment. . . . Whenever we took Tanya, Dorothy would say, 'Oh, Frank, do win me a coconut.' SOBS – 8 SEC. . . . I didn't even think. This afternoon Tanya wanted to go to the fair and . . . SOBS – 11 SEC. . . . Simon?
SIMON . . . I'm still here.
FRANK SOBS – 4 SEC. . . . Tanya said, 'Win me a coconut, daddy.'
SIMON . . . Yes?

FRANK ... Can you imagine? I was shattered, Simon. God knows, I tried, I really tried, but ... SOBS – 14 SEC. ... I couldn't win. ... Seven pounds fifty, and I still couldn't win Tanya a coconut.

PAUSE IN CONVERSATION – 6 SEC.

SIMON No.

FRANK SOBS – 7 SEC.

SIMON What are you doing tonight?

FRANK ... Tonight, tomorrow ... next week? God knows!

SIMON ... I'm on my way to Redhill. I'll pick up some booze and drop by for an hour if you like.

FRANK Oh, yes. ... Simon ... thank you. SOBS – 4 SEC. ... Thank you.

SIMON ... Frank?

FRANK ... Yes?

SIMON I've never been able to win a coconut.

FRANK BIG SOBS – 18 SEC.

SIMON See you soon.

CALL 202 – TIMED 19.04 – THE SAME DAY

RORY WEBB:
(ANSWERING) Hello?

SIMON WEBB:
... Rory?

RORY Hi, dad. I've only just managed to hitch back. Where is everyone?

SIMON ... They must be still round at Val's.

RORY Yeah?

SIMON Tell your mother I'm going to see George and might be late, would you?

RORY Sure.

SIMON ... See you then.

RORY ... Some homecoming!

SIMON What do you want, massed pipes?

RORY	. . . Everything all right, dad?
SIMON	It's the first day of forever.
RORY	. . . What?
SIMON	. . . Bye, Rory.
RORY	. . . Dad?
	DEAD LINE

CALL 203 – TIMED 19.18 – THE SAME DAY

RORY WEBB:
(ANSWERING) Hello?
JOANNA WEBB:
Rory! Darling! . . . How are you?

RORY	. . . Just made it home.
JOANNA	Lovely. I'm so sorry I wasn't there. Rather overstayed at Val's. Mother started putting the pro-nuclear case.
RORY	. . . Gran's staying with Val?
JOANNA	No, no. She's having a little rest with us.
RORY	. . . So I'm sharing with Kit?
JOANNA	. . . Kit's left home.
RORY	. . . *What*?
JOANNA	. . . Yes.
RORY	. . . I don't believe it!
JOANNA	. . . Rory . . . we won't be long. I wanted to let your father know we're on our way.
RORY	Oh! Dad just phoned to say he'd be late.
JOANNA	. . . Late?
RORY	He's gone to see George.
JOANNA	. . . I see.
RORY	. . . What is it with Dad? . . . He's sounding . . . desperate.
	PAUSE IN CONVERSATION – 4 SEC.
JOANNA	He's just exhausted.
RORY	Yeah? . . . It was really weird getting back, mum. . . . I'm not sure about the indoor forest.
JOANNA	. . . Don't mention it in front of mother.

RORY I wouldn't mention it in front of anyone.
JOANNA . . . No.
RORY See you soon.
JOANNA Lovely, dear. . . . Goodbye.

CALL 204 – TIMED 19.36 – THE SAME DAY

RORY WEBB:
(ANSWERING) Hello?
KIT WEBB:
Rory!
RORY Great! Kit? . . . Terrific!
KIT . . . Yeah.
RORY . . . Right.
KIT You got back okay?
RORY It was some hitch from Gatwick. I'd spent my last note on booze. I mean . . . there I was, blue and white scarf, a bag of duty-frees and a cut face. Who's going to pick that up?
KIT Thicko!
RORY True. I walked God knows how far. Then a car-load of Chelsea supporters stopped. It was one hell of a hitch.
KIT Jeez!
RORY Forget your duty-frees.
KIT I wasn't exactly banking on them.
RORY Right. . . . What's up with dad?
KIT . . . Dad's there?
RORY Nobody's here. Dad phoned in and sounds like . . . like he's just given up. . . . He told me it wasn't you who told him about me telling you I wasn't mugged. . . . You've talked to him?
KIT Talked to him? *Nobody* can talk to him. Dad's gone zombie.
RORY . . . Yeah?
KIT . . . Listen, can't be long. I'm *As U Like Itting*

and I've got to keep an eye out for Wanda. It's just that mum's set up lunch tomorrow with dad and the whole damned family. We're looking at one long disaster. . . . Tell her we're coming.

RORY Will do.

KIT . . . You'll get to meet Dustin.

RORY Sure. . . . Who's Dustin?

KIT . . . My flat-share.

RORY . . . Yeah?

KIT . . . Yeah.

PAUSE IN CONVERSATION – 5 SEC.

RORY I'm with you.

KIT . . . Would that dad was.

RORY You're . . . safe?

KIT . . . Fine. . . . It's a first for both of us.

RORY Right. . . . We'll see you tomorrow, yeah?

KIT Looks like it.

RORY . . . Hey, what do you think dad'll say? There was no one here when I got back so I had to break that small window . . .

KIT Sort it out with Dustin.

RORY . . . Yeah?

KIT See you, Rory.

RORY . . . Yeah.

CALL 205 – TIMED 20.12 – THE SAME DAY

TANYA GRISEWOOD:
Hello . . . ? Mum . . . ?

FERN WEBB:
(PHONING OUT) It's Fern, Tanya.

TANYA . . . Oh . . .

FERN I'm glad we all met up at the fair.

TANYA . . . It was awful.

FERN Yeah, but I got home and Rory's back! Rory! Dad made him hitch from Gatwick and he's wrecked. He's put his Chelsea scarf in with my Miles Ton T-shirts to help the starving.

TANYA . . . *Everyone*'s wrecked. Your father came round to cheer mine up.

FERN Yeah?

TANYA Dad's gone to have a lie down.

FERN . . . He didn't enjoy the fair much. Does he always cry if he doesn't win something?

TANYA . . . It was awful.

FERN Who was the greasy guy who tried to sell him drugs?

TANYA Dunno. . . . Fern, why should I be very, very strong? Dad let your grandmum scare off the pusher, while he stayed sobbing over a slot-machine.

FERN Yeah.

TANYA . . . What did your grandmum mean?

FERN When?

TANYA She said it wasn't her usual Easter.

FERN . . . Perhaps they don't have a fair in Ludlow.

TANYA . . . No?

FERN Oh, Tanya! Tanya! Come to lunch tomorrow. You can look at Rory.

TANYA Wow!

FERN He's a real mess. . . . MUM?

PAUSE IN CONVERSATION – 52 SEC.

JOANNA WEBB:

Tanya, dear?

TANYA Hi, Mrs Webb.

JOANNA Why don't you and your father both come tomorrow? You must be . . . uh. . . . We'd love you to come.

TANYA Yeah? . . . I'll go and ask dad.

PAUSE IN CONVERSATION – 2 MIN 37 SEC.

Mrs Webb?

JOANNA . . . Yes?

TANYA Dad says he supposes even your house if it gets us out of this bloody place.

JOANNA . . . Well . . . that's lovely, dear.

TANYA Great.

JOANNA We'll see you tomorrow, then.
TANYA Sure.
JOANNA . . . Goodbye, Tanya.
TANYA Bye, Mrs Webb.

CALL 206 – TIMED 23.43 – THE SAME DAY

JOANNA WEBB:
(ANSWERING) Hello?
GEORGE MEADOWS:
. . . 'Lo?
JOANNA . . . Yes?
GEORGE . . . 'Lo?
JOANNA . . . Who's that speaking?
GEORGE . . . That . . . J'anna?
JOANNA Yes. Who's . . . ?
GEORGE J'anna?
JOANNA . . . Yes. . . . George.
GEORGE . . . Simon's . . .
JOANNA . . . Yes?
GEORGE . . . Simon's . . .
JOANNA . . . Drunk?
GEORGE . . . Simon's . . .
JOANNA Yes?
GEORGE . . . staying . . . the night.
JOANNA I see.
GEORGE . . . He . . . says . . .
DEAD LINE

SUNDAY 30 MARCH

CALL 207 – TIMED 12.51

SALLY WIMBUSH:
Hello?
JOANNA WEBB:
(PHONING OUT) Sally? It's Joanna.

SALLY Joanna . . . we're just on our way over.

JOANNA Lovely. I was wondering if we could beg some plates. The posh service went with the burglars and I've only just realized how many we're. . . . Good heavens! Someone's at the door. . . . *Rory? Answer the. . . . Right*. . . . Sally?

SALLY . . . I'll bring some plates.

JOANNA Bless you. . . . Gracious, Frank's here! It's not even twelve.

SALLY . . . It's nearly one.

JOANNA . . . What?

SALLY The clocks have gone forward.

JOANNA Oh, no! . . . *Frank, I'm so glad you could make it. . . . I think Fern's upstairs, Tanya. . . . Rory, find mother. . . . I'm afraid Simon's not back yet.*

SALLY . . . How many plates?

JOANNA Uh . . . half a dozen?

SALLY Fine.

JOANNA *Mother? . . . Oh, yes, I'd forgotten you'd met Frank.*

SALLY . . . See you soon.

JOANNA Lovely, Sally. . . . *Mother, I'm sure Frank doesn't want to be reminded . . .*

CALL 208 – TIMED 14.14 – THE SAME DAY

***RUNAROUND MINIS'* CONTROLLER:**
. . . *realize it's Easter morning. . . . Runaround Minis.*

KIT WEBB:
(PHONING OUT) It's 24, Tufnell Park Terrace. Could we have a car to Paddington?

CONTROLLER . . . Any flat number?

KIT It's an old lady. She's sitting on a case in the porch.

CONTROLLER . . . Right.

KIT Can you make it fairly soon?

CONTROLLER . . . *expect the earth. . . .* Five minutes.

KIT Okay.

CONTROLLER . . . *Car 8?*

CALL 209 – TIMED 14.39 – THE SAME DAY

MICHAEL WEBB:
(ANSWERING) Hello?

SIMON WEBB:
. . . Who's that?

MICHAEL Simon, you sod! It's Michael. Where the blazes are you?

SIMON . . . I'm still in Redhill.

MICHAEL Christ! Simon, no one deserves this! You've got a houseful here.

SIMON . . . I'm only just up. . . . Let me speak to Joanna.

MICHAEL . . . She's gone to bed.

SIMON . . . She's . . . ?

MICHAEL Things got rather out of control. The moment I walked through the door your mother-in-law had a pink fit. . . . She's still sitting in the porch.

SIMON . . . Why?

MICHAEL God knows! She asked Sally if I really performed Satanic rites with a dozen naked couples at full moon. Sally said yes and what a pity there wasn't a full moon.

SIMON Oh! . . . Of course.

MICHAEL Kate shot off muttering about the inadequacy of our penal system and packed her bags.

SIMON . . . And Joanna's in bed?

MICHAEL Migraine. She's not a little upset. . . . Hold on. Kit wants a word.

KIT WEBB:

Dad? You're a grade one prat!

SIMON . . . There's no need . . .

KIT Where are you? Fern's spent all morning painting you an egg, Grisewood's boring Dustin out of his mind with . . .

SIMON Frank's there?

BEDROOM PHONE CONNECTING

JOANNA WEBB:

Simon?

KIT Mum, he's a bastard!

SIMON Get off the line, Kit. I want to speak to your mother.

KIT Everyone drags themselves out of bed to get here . . .

JOANNA:

Kit!

KIT Okay, okay. It's just that . . . where the hell's dad?

JOANNA:

Please, Kit.

KIT Okay.

PAUSE IN CONVERSATION – 4 SEC.

JOANNA Where the hell are you, Simon?

SIMON . . . I'm still in Redhill.

JOANNA Surely you could . . . ?

FERN WEBB:

Dad?

SIMON Fern, I'm talking to your mother.

FERN:

Dustin wants to know if you'd like the window repaired again.

SIMON The window . . . ?

FERN:

Hang on, the minicab's here. . . . ***BYE, GRANDMUM. . . . HAVE A GOOD JOURNEY.***

JOANNA . . . Fern?

FERN:

Yeah?

JOANNA Did your grandmother say anything?

FERN:

She said, 'Thank heavens!'

SIMON Fern, get off the line!

FERN:

Rory's here.

RORY WEBB:

Mum?

JOANNA . . . Yes, dear?

RORY:

Now Kate's gone, is it okay if I get Kit's room and Fern gets mine?

JOANNA Rory! She's barely out of the door!

RORY:

She was pretty firm about not coming back.

SIMON Get off the line, Rory!

RORY:

Hi, dad. It'd be nice to see you sometime.

SIMON Rory, put the damned phone down.

RORY:

Happy Easter!

HALL PHONE DISCONNECTING

SIMON . . . Joanna?

JOANNA . . . Yes?

SIMON . . . I'm not coming back?

JOANNA . . . What?

HALL PHONE CONNECTING

MICHAEL WEBB:

Joanna? Look, Sally's terribly upset. She never realized Kate was being serious.

JOANNA ... What did you say, Simon?

SIMON ... I'm not coming back.

JOANNA You're not ... ?

SIMON I'm staying here a couple of nights, then moving in with Michael.

MICHAEL:

Uh. ... It was a lovely meal, Joanna. I'll be downstairs.

HALL PHONE DISCONNECTING

SIMON ... Joanna?

JOANNA ... Yes?

SIMON ... I know about Curtis.

JOANNA ... Curtis ... ?

HALL PHONE CONNECTING

KIT WEBB:

Mum? Grisewood says goodbye. He's taking Tanya home to calm down. ... Mum?

JOANNA ... Say goodbye to Frank for me.

KIT:

How's the migraine?

JOANNA ... Better.

KIT:

You don't sound better.

JOANNA Kit ... let me talk to your father.

KIT:

Sooner you than me.

HALL PHONE DISCONNECTING

PAUSE IN CONVERSATION – 6 SEC.

JOANNA Simon?

SIMON ... Yes?

JOANNA ... What do you mean?

SIMON I mean that's it, Joanna!

DEAD LINE

MONDAY 31 MARCH

CALL 210 – TIMED 11.43

JOANNA WEBB:
(ANSWERING) Hello?
VAL JESSOP
Awwgh! . . . Joanna?

JOANNA . . . Yes?
VAL *Urcht!* . . . I thought you'd never answer. . . . *Urcht!*
JOANNA . . . Sorry.
VAL I'm all but done with the *Post-Nuclear*. I was wondering if Fern could face that last sitting?
JOANNA . . . Uh. . . . Rory's taken her off for the day.
VAL . . . Not to worry. *Eeugh!* . . . *Urcht! Oogph!* . . . Joanna, you don't sound very well.
JOANNA . . . I'm fine.
VAL . . . And how's Simon?
JOANNA . . . He's . . . he's away too.
VAL You're all by yourself?
JOANNA . . . Yes. . . . Yes. . . . I'm fine.
PAUSE IN CONVERSATION – 5 SEC.
VAL What's wrong?
JOANNA . . . Val . . . ?
VAL . . . Yes, heart.
JOANNA . . . I'll phone.
VAL . . . Yes?
JOANNA . . . Yes.
VAL . . . Joanna, are you sure . . . ?

JOANNA Goodbye, Val.
VAL . . . Yes. . . . Goodbye, heart.

CALL 211 – TIMED 15.24 – THE SAME DAY

WANDA POOL:
Hi.
KIT WEBB:
(PHONING OUT) Hi, Wanda. It's Kit. Thanks for coming Saturday.

WANDA Kit! Yeah. . . . The *As U Like It*'s amazing. I've been filling in Big Gut and Elastoplast.
KIT . . . We tell everyone they won't believe the place. They don't.
WANDA Right.
KIT . . . You all packed up?
WANDA There's not a lot to pack. Jason says all you need when travelling's an open mind.
KIT I wouldn't bank on it, Wanda.
WANDA No?
KIT How's Jason going to cope without you to bum off?
WANDA He says Gandhi managed with just one spare loin-cloth. Yeah, and he's taking a course in pyramid selling.
KIT . . . Where is that guy?
WANDA I don't care where he is, as long as he's not in France.
KIT Right. . . . Oh, yeah, dad's finally goofed.
WANDA Yeah?
KIT He's crashed out with some cronies. We came round to repair the window and found mum catatonic. I told her she ought to hit town and celebrate.
WANDA . . . I'm trying to think what Jason would say.
KIT Mum's got enough problems, Wanda.
WANDA Sure.

KIT	. . . Listen, thanks for the birthday prezzie. . . . Jeez, oh, Jeez! . . . I've never even thanked mum for the cufflinks.
WANDA	Cufflinks?
KIT	Yeah. My eighteenth was such a mess, she sent them on to me. They're pretty neat cufflinks.
WANDA	Yeah?
KIT	. . . Your sweat-shirt's great too.
WANDA	Anytime. . . . You're sounding good, Kit.
KIT	I'm okay.
WANDA	Keep it that way, yes?
KIT	I'll try. Be nice to *Les Amis Universels*.
WANDA	Will do.
KIT	. . . Hope the journey's good.
WANDA	. . . I'll write.
KIT	. . . Neither will I.
WANDA	Sure.
KIT	Yeah.
WANDA	. . . Bye, Kit.
KIT	. . . Yeah. . . . Bye, Wanda.
WANDA	. . . Chaio . . . uh. . . . Goodbye.
KIT	. . . Yeah.

CALL 212 – TIMED 18.46 – THE SAME DAY

FERN WEBB:
(ANSWERING) Hello?
TANYA GRISEWOOD:
Fern! Fern! Mum's back!

FERN	Wow!
TANYA	It's the best! I don't have to be strong any more.
FERN	Where's she been?
TANYA	Dunno. She just walked in while dad was trying to get the dishwasher working and said not to worry, she'd take care of it. Mum always knows who to phone.

FERN Great.

TANYA They think everything'll be all right if we move, and dad says anywhere's okay as long as it's miles away from the bloody Webbs. . . . Can you come round?

FERN Rory's taking me to get new videos. He's being really nice, 'cause dad's still having a little rest with friends.

TANYA Hang-on. . . . *WHAT? . . . IT'S FERN!*
PAUSE IN CONVERSATION – 8 SEC
Bye, Fern.
DEAD LINE

CALL 213 – TIMED 19.33 – THE SAME DAY

KATE AGNEW:
Hello, Ludlow (NUMBER WITHHELD).
JOANNA WEBB:
(PHONING OUT) . . . Mother?

KATE Joanna, hello. I'm not fond of the phone ringing. Ronald's little red light blinks. It'll have to go.

JOANNA . . . Yes. . . . Do you have a moment?

KATE How wise of your husband to boycott the coven. If Simon won't sit down to dinner with his own brother, Joanna, I do feel you ought to think twice.

JOANNA . . . Mother . . . may I talk to you?

KATE Of course. So much better for me to have come back. So much to do, dear. I've decided to fill in the fish-pond.

JOANNA . . . I wanted to have a chat . . . about Simon.

KATE Yes, dear? You've no idea how enervating it is to make a clean sweep. I've been wondering about planning permission. Would it be possible for me to *build* in the garden?

JOANNA . . . I've no idea, mother.

KATE . . . How is Simon?

JOANNA . . . He's . . . very well.

KATE Good.

JOANNA . . . I was just making sure you got back all right.

KATE . . . Well, I did, dear.

JOANNA . . . Yes.

KATE . . . We'll say goodbye then.

JOANNA . . . Yes.

KATE . . . Goodbye.

JOANNA . . . Goodbye, mother.

TUESDAY 1 APRIL

CALL 214 – TIMED 10.12

JOANNA WEBB:
(ANSWERING) Hello?
SIMON WEBB:
. . . Joanna?

JOANNA	. . . Yes?
SIMON	. . . I'm dropping back to pick up a few things.
	PAUSE IN CONVERSATION – 4 SEC.
JOANNA	When?
SIMON	Later this afternoon.
JOANNA	. . . Right.
SIMON	I'll be going on to Michael's.
JOANNA	. . . I see.
SIMON	. . . Yes.
JOANNA	. . . Fine.
SIMON	Good.
JOANNA	There's some letters here for you. . . . *Clover Cover Insurance*, the Metropolitan Police . . . and the bank.
	PAUSE IN CONVERSATION – 6 SEC.
SIMON	I'll pick them up.
JOANNA	. . . Simon. . . . I shan't be here.
SIMON	. . . Right.
JOANNA	. . . Goodbye.
SIMON	Yes. . . . Goodbye, Joanna.

CALL 215 – TIMED 10.33 – THE SAME DAY

KIT WEBB:
Webb and Caroway.

RORY WEBB:
(PHONING OUT) Kit?

KIT Hi, Rory.

RORY Just tell me what the hell's happened?

KIT . . . How d'you mean?

RORY I mean I wave goodbye to a standard, tight-assed, moderately responsible family . . . come back a year later and walk into a five act tragedy.

KIT . . . Right.

RORY Mum's packing. She's taking Fern and going to stay with Val.

KIT . . . Yeah?

RORY . . . Why?

KIT You don't know what dad's been like, Rory. Nobody can take it any more.

RORY . . . Some mess.

KIT . . . Sure.

RORY It's getting pretty lonely here, Kit. What was Wanda's squat like?

KIT One problem. It's got a built-in philosophical bullshit dispenser.

RORY Jason?

KIT Jason.

RORY . . . Dad's coming back to pick up his things. I'll have to talk to him.

KIT You can try. I don't think he's listened to a word anyone's said in weeks.

RORY . . . Yeah?

KIT . . . See you.

RORY . . . Yeah.

CALL 216 – TIMED 11.46 – THE SAME DAY

JOANNA WEBB:
(ANSWERING) Hello?
CURTIS PINE:
Joanna?

JOANNA Curtis? . . . Where are you?
CURTIS . . . M25. Jammed in a contraflow.
JOANNA . . . I'm impressed.
CURTIS Impressed? Stick around, Joanna. Everything's worked out. *Pix Trix* bought it.
JOANNA That's . . .
CURTIS They've bought the game and they've bought me to go with it. I'll be moving base to the States.
JOANNA . . . That's wonderful.
CURTIS . . . Hold on. The traffic's unblocked.
PAUSE IN CONVERSATION – 14 SEC.
Joanna? . . . *Get out of the* . . . . . . I can't thank you enough.
PAUSE IN CONVERSATION – 17 SEC.
. . . only person I could talk to. Either people knew the business and I couldn't trust . . . *Move over you* . . . *Damned Volkswagen*!
PAUSE IN CONVERSATION – 4 SEC.
JOANNA Hello?
PAUSE IN CONVERSATION – 12 SEC.
CURTIS . . . or they thought I was a raving nutter. You saved my sanity, Joanna. Let's . . . *Bloody truck*! . . . Let's meet.
JOANNA Curtis . . . no. . . . I'm leaving Simon.
CURTIS . . . Why?
JOANNA . . . He thinks we were having an affair.
CURTIS *What*? . . . LAUGHS – 6 SEC.
JOANNA Curtis?
CURTIS LAUGHS – 11 SEC.
JOANNA Hello?
CURTIS LAUGHS – 9 SEC.
CRASH – 23 SEC.

JOANNA Curtis! . . . Curtis!
CURTIS . . . Hello?
JOANNA What's happened?
CURTIS LAUGHS – 8 SEC. . . . hard shoulder facing the wrong way.
JOANNA . . . Are you all right?
CURTIS . . . Fine. Absolutely fine.
JOANNA . . . Well . . . I'm thrilled everything worked out for you.
CURTIS It's only a game.
JOANNA . . . Yes.
CURTIS . . . I'll let you know how things go.
JOANNA . . . All right.
CURTIS Meanwhile, I'm in a bit of a mess here. I'd better . . .
JOANNA Goodbye, Curtis.
CURTIS . . . Joanna?
JOANNA . . . Goodbye.
CURTIS . . . Goodbye, Joanna.

CALL 217 – TIMED 16.04 – THE SAME DAY

RORY WEBB:
(ANSWERING) Hello?
NORMAN HOOPER:
Mr Webb there?
RORY Sure. Who's that?
NORMAN It's Norman. *All Star Garage*.
RORY Right. . . . *DAD*?
PAUSE IN CONVERSATION – 6 SEC.
IT'S NORMAN! . . . Hold on. . . . *ALL STAR GARAGE*! . . . He's down in the basement. I'll get him.
PAUSE IN CONVERSATION – 2 MIN 19 SEC.
Sorry, dad's out.
NORMAN Yeah? . . . Tell him his cheque's bounced and he'll be hearing, will you?
RORY . . . Sure.

NORMAN . . . Cheers.
RORY . . . Bye.

CALL 218 – TIMED 16.19 – THE SAME DAY

VAL JESSOP:
Urcht!
SIMON WEBB:
(PHONING OUT) Val? . . . It's Simon here.
VAL *Awwgh!*
SIMON . . . Could I speak to Joanna?
VAL . . . I will . . . *Oogph!* . . . ask her.
PAUSE IN CONVERSATION – 49 SEC.
JOANNA WEBB:
Hello?
SIMON . . . Joanna?
JOANNA . . . Yes?
PAUSE IN CONVERSATION – 6 SEC.
SIMON I've made a terrible mistake.
JOANNA No.
SIMON . . . No?
JOANNA . . . It's a good idea to finish, Simon. I can't do any more . . . and I certainly can't take any more.
SIMON . . . But it's all been my fault.
JOANNA . . . Yes.
PAUSE IN CONVERSATION – 9 SEC.
SIMON Joanna . . . come back.
DEAD LINE

CALL 219 – TIMED 23.31 – THE SAME DAY

MICHAEL WEBB:
Simon?

SIMON WEBB:

(PHONING OUT) . . . Whah . . .?

MICHAEL Simon, where the hell are you? We thought you'd be here.

SIMON . . . no . . . point . . .

MICHAEL . . . What's happened?

SIMON . . . no . . . point . . .

MICHAEL Simon, sober up!

SIMON . . . no money . . . no job . . . no J'anna . . .

MICHAEL Where's Joanna?

SIMON . . . gone . . . gone, gone, gone . . .

MICHAEL Listen, Simon, I'll come round.

SIMON . . . no . . . point . . .

MICHAEL Is anyone with you?

SIMON . . . Rory . . . good ol' Rory . . . Rory . . .

MICHAEL . . . Simon?

SIMON . . . bedtime . . . up the wooden . . . sleep . . . sleep . . . sleep . . .

DEAD LINE

WEDNESDAY 2 APRIL

CALL 220 – TIMED 11.47

OPERATOR:
British Telecom International.
SIMON WEBB:
(PHONING OUT) Hello? I wanted to check a number.

OPERATOR Which country?
SIMON . . . France.
OPERATOR Thank you.
PAUSE IN CONVERSATION – 11 SEC.
Which town?
SIMON Grenoble.
OPERATOR . . . The name?
SIMON *Les Amis Universels.*
OPERATOR *Les Amis Universels,* Grenoble.
SIMON . . . Yes.
PAUSE IN CONVERSATION – 32 SEC.
OPERATOR The number is (NUMBER WITHHELD).
SIMON . . . Thanks.

CALL 221 – TIMED 12.14 – THE SAME DAY

KIT WEBB:
Webb and Caroway.

RORY WEBB:
(PHONING OUT) Kit?

KIT . . . What's the latest?
RORY You've got a bed-sized piece of floor I could crash on? I need out of here, Kit.
KIT . . . I'd have to get clearance.
RORY Tell Dustin I'm desperate. . . . Yesterday dad comes back and . . . What's with the basement? We've got a whole empty house and he goes and sits in the basement . . . finally emerges and kicks shit out of a skirting-board.
KIT . . . So what's new?
RORY . . . He told the goose he needs to find peace somewhere.
KIT . . . Yeah?
RORY I ask you, *peace*? There's no one else here. I've got to get out.
KIT . . . Yeah. . . . Hold on. I'll find Dustin.
PAUSE IN CONVERSATION – 1 MIN 38 SEC.
It's a very temporary stay, right?
RORY What isn't?
KIT . . . Right.
RORY I'll be round this afternoon.
KIT . . . See you.
RORY . . . Thanks, Kit.

CALL 222 – TIMED 12.53 – THE SAME DAY

SIMON WEBB:
(PHONING OUT) Hello?
LES AMIS UNIVERSELS RECORDED ANSWER:
Bonjour. Vous êtes bien au (NUMBER WITHHELD). *Les Amis Universels* sont désolés de ne pouvoir prendre votre appel en personne. Laissez vos coordonnées, et nous vous rappèlerons dès que possible. Veuillez

parler après la tonalité. Merci. . . . And to our English friends, hello. We are afraid that there is no one here at the moment . . .
DEAD LINE